With Passion,
We Live and Love

Research, Prose, Verse and Music

by

Alex Bennet and Cindy Lee Scott

MQIPress (2019)

Frost, West Virginia

ISBN 978-1-949829-35-8

MQIPress
Frost, West Virginia
303 Mountain Quest Lane, Marlinton, WV 24954
United States of America
Telephone: 304-799-7267
eMail: alex@mountainquestinstitute.com
www.mountainquestinstitute.com
www.mountainquestinn.com
www.MQIPress.com
www.Myst-Art.com

ISBN 978-1-949829-35-8
Cover picture by Alex Bennet

Preface

Alex and Cindy are sisters. They met four years ago. If you've read any of Cindy Lee Scott's verse, you may already know their story. Alex was given for adoption as an infant along with an older sister, and Cindy, 15 months younger than Alex, was raised by their birth mother. Up into her seventies, Alex did not know Cindy existed. But Cindy knew about the others, with a growing awareness as she repeatedly heard her mother sob into the dark hours of the morning. Many years later, Cindy expressed and shared this in verse titled "Never Meant to Be":

Born out of love, and never meant to be
Steeped in betrayal, it's all she could see
Denied by blood, left with children of love
No help coming from below or above.

How can she live and survive without him?
With blameless sweet children born into sin
Nowhere to turn and her world upside down
A heart wrenching pain, with no one around.

What can she do with everything wrong?
Needs to be met and funds won't last long
How can she choose which ones to let go?
A lifetime of sadness she will soon know.

Tears will fall silent as time moves on by
While inside she's throbbing and sobbing: **Why?**
The soul's pain is dulled by the sting of death
In quiet strength the secret breathes its last breath.

In March of 2016, her 68th year of life, Cindy located a document on Ancestry about her mother with the incorrect death date of 1947 (a year before Cindy was born!) The reference also noted that a daughter named Cleo Barbara (who would have been her older older-sister) was deceased. Cindy sent off a note to correct her mother's date of death and to ask about any connections to Cleo Barbara, providing her personal email. She received a quick response from an "Alex", who was Cleo Barbara's younger sister (and Cindy's older sister)! Thus began our story, which is expressed in a larger fashion in Cindy's collection of verse titled *Painting the Reality of My Soul*, available from amazon.com.

Cindy, a flower child of the 60's, is a veracious poet grown through a wide diversity of life experiences. Verse gave direction to and expression for her passion, and coupled with music and faith, served as the saving grace of her life. During that same time period, Alex was forging ahead in her life, yes, also filled with the strong passions of young life, while entangled with government work. Alex's hunger for knowledge led to taking a consilience approach in her studies. Writing continuously, primarily prose and largely non-fiction, she is widely published. So, while taking different forms, both sisters are prolific writers.

A second strong commonality is all three sister's passionate love for, and life involvement in, music, Cleo Barbara (the oldest) as a violinist, pianist, vocalist and guitarist; Alex (second born) as a flautist and opera singer; and Cindy (the youngest) as a pianist, vocalist, guitarist, harpist and composer. And there are so many other characteristics that can be tied to genetics, having more to do with the depth of emotions and feelings and the way we process life events. Interesting study of nature and nurture!

That brings us to this book, which explores in prose and verse—through logic and emotion—aspects and characteristics of passion and love and the remarkable role they play in living. In this book we offer some of poet Cindy Lee Scott's early verse not previously published, the prose and poetry of a young heart searching for meaning, often through sexual encounters connected to strong feelings that were not reciprocated. And we also offer several prose pieces from Alex's early life, never before shared. From both … so much passion. So much learning. So much living.

We hope you enjoy this sharing, and that somehow it helps each of us better understand ourselves.

With love and appreciation, Alex Bennet and Cindy Lee Scott

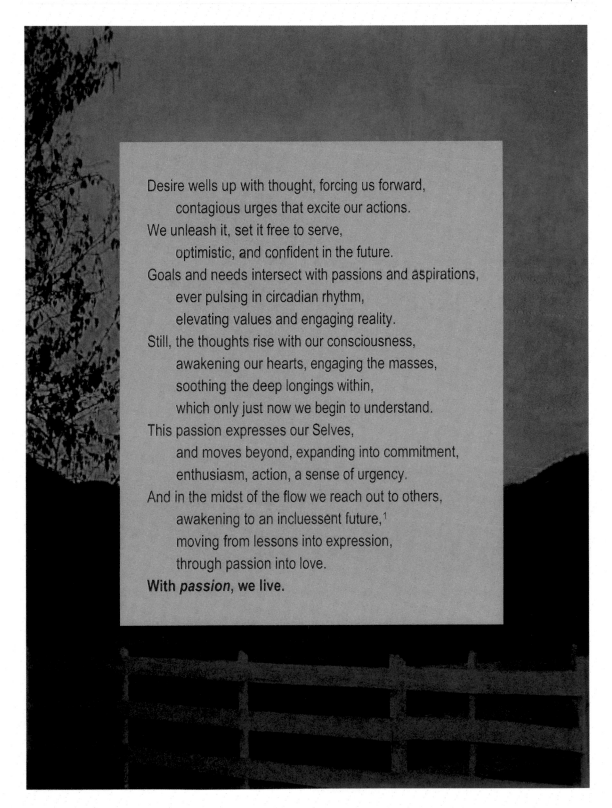

Desire wells up with thought, forcing us forward,
 contagious urges that excite our actions.
We unleash it, set it free to serve,
 optimistic, and confident in the future.
Goals and needs intersect with passions and aspirations,
 ever pulsing in circadian rhythm,
 elevating values and engaging reality.
Still, the thoughts rise with our consciousness,
 awakening our hearts, engaging the masses,
 soothing the deep longings within,
 which only just now we begin to understand.
This passion expresses our Selves,
 and moves beyond, expanding into commitment,
 enthusiasm, action, a sense of urgency.
And in the midst of the flow we reach out to others,
 awakening to an incluessent future,[1]
 moving from lessons into expression,
 through passion into love.
With *passion*, we live.

Contents

Ah, life! What is it all about? Certainly, "love" is a good and wise answer. Only, in different situations we use the word love to mean so many different things. And while we like to think of ourselves living in a field of love—and indeed that may be the case—there is a driver in human emotions that, when coupled with love, gives us purpose and moves us beyond ourselves toward a greater good. That driver might be called *passion.*

Have you ever wondered why you have stronger emotions about doing one thing over another, or for one person over another, or even for wearing a specific color? These preferences are the seeding of passion, or even the expression of passion. So, what exactly is passion? Where does it come from? How does it affect us? And what does that connection between passion and love look like?

While we'll explore various definitions of passion both current and historical in Chapter 1, it's a good idea to have a common understanding right up front of what this word represents. So, for purposes of this little book, *passion is considered a term to indicate those desires, behaviors, and thoughts that suggest urges with considerable force.*[2] Characteristics of those urges specifically include the assertation that positive passions affirm that something is precious, and that passion can be used as a determinant of what is of higher interest and great.[3] Thus, positive passion is used to indicate value, and passion, whether positive or negative, is used as a determinant of what is of higher interest to an individual.

Ah, and that brings us back to love, a very special frequency that weaves through every aspect of our Universe and, when allowed, every aspect of us. How on Earth to define this amazing concept? So many ways. We could certainly talk about it as physical, as an emotion in terms of chemicals and molecules that activate the body's responses to emotional arousal. Or, we could talk about love as a transmitter of the meaning of information in terms of feelings and emotions.

That begs the question: Are feelings and emotions the same thing? One differentiation is the use of the term "feelings" to represent the private mental experience of emotion, and the use of the term "emotions" to represent those public expressions of response.[4] The passion model introduced in Chapter 2 emerges from this distinction, that is, grouping characteristics of passion in terms of *externally observed* and *internally felt*.

> "Feelings" represent the private mental experience of emotion, and the use of the term "emotions" represents those public expressions of response. Passion is often a part of both.

There is so much more to say about love, and if you are old enough to be reading this, you will no doubt have experienced love, whether consciously or unconsciously, so you could help us create an understanding of that term. Perhaps the discussion in Chapter III will reflect some of your own thoughts and experiences.

As no doubt we have all experienced, passion as an emotion can drive our experiences negatively as well as positively, especially when we allow it to be the sole driver of that experience without any balancing from mental resources. This highlights the importance of the body of work on Emotional Intelligence[5] and much work that focuses on the value of emotions as a guidance system. Emotional Intelligence is the ability to sense, understand, and effectively apply the power and acumen of emotions as a source of human energy, information, connection and influence. It includes self-control as well as zeal and persistence (passion), and the ability to motivate oneself.

In the Conscious Look Book *Possibilities that are YOU! Volume 14: The Emoting Guidance System*, the first idea presented focuses on emotions and feelings as a guidance system for survival and the pain and pleasure portals of personality, and a building block of consciousness. Emotions are essential to living and the quality of life. As Henry Plotkin asserts, "Normal human life is lived within a sea of experienced and expressed emotions."[6] And it is passion, *those forceful desires, behaviors, and thoughts,* that direct and value our lives, our living.

We begin this little book by taking a deeper dive into the concept of passion, and then share a passion model that groups the characteristics attributed to passion. Next, we explore the passion of love, which indeed touches passions of the body, head and spirit, each of which is dedicated a chapter which features the verse of Cindy Lee Scott. We also look at passion in terms of leadership, and suggest that thought leaders in their fields of endeavor are largely driven by passion. Finally, we explore the connection between passion and music before ending with moments and events suggestive of living from the heart.

This is indeed a strange book circling around passion. Taking a consilience approach, you will discover research that crosses the fields of neuroscience, psychology, music, management, and spirituality, with poetry and prose punctuating that research. Then, there are stories capturing moments of passion, many never before shared. And music expressing moments of passion.

And, along the way, we share life bites of our selves, perhaps reflective of some of your own experiences in life, and perhaps not. There is so much more to be written!

We hope you enjoy this journey with us.

With passion and love,
Alex Bennet and Cindy Lee Scott

I: The Gift of Passion

No doubt passion has been around as long as we've known we were humans—or perhaps even longer!

Each of us is unique, that is, YOU are one of a kind! Think about that for a moment. Even if you have an identical twin, from the instant of conception your experiences—even while in womb because of differing entangled relationships (fetus placement, fluid flows, sound waves, etc.)—are unique to you. And the longer we live, through our experiences and the thoughts and feelings spurred by those experiences, we create a self that has preferences (likes and dislikes) and the ability to participate in choosing what we want to experience in the future.

And that brings us to passion, which is that *gift of emotion* that causes us to take a precise interest in, and pay keen attention to,[7] specific aspects of our lives; to open us up to the larger picture;[8] and, even, to promote the greater good.[9] As Peter Senge so eloquently says, passion is directly connected to the "deep longing of human beings to make a difference," to contribute.[10] Passion, then, appears to have the potential to be an indicator of value to each of us, and can be directly linked to those larger things that each of us as a "self" feels are important.

Some History

In a historical context, the word "passions" (in the plural) appears in Plato's *Dialogues* and Aristotle's *Rhetoric*, as well as in the Greek discussions of virtue and vice, to represent emotions. Ancient Greek philosophers had a propensity to indulge both their reason and passions alike, in the hopes of perfecting the former and outgrowing the latter.[11]

The term "passions" also appears in the moral theology of Thomas Aquinas and in Benedict Spinoza's *Ethics*; and in books of political theory, such as Niccolo

Machiavelli's *The Prince* and Thomas Hobbes' *Leviathan*.[12] And René Descartes' "six 'primitive' passions—**wonder, love, hatred, desire, joy, and sadness**—are not meaningless agitations of the animal spirits, but ingredients in the good life."[13] [emphasis added]

> *The primitive passions—wonder, love, hatred, desire, joy and sadness—are ingredients in the good life.*
>
> -René Descartes

Descartes described these primitive passions as **passions of the soul**, sensitive moments in life representing a connection or union between the body and soul, which was located in the pineal gland actively engaged in overseeing all the functions of the human body. These passions of the soul fill the prose, poetry and music that punctuate this book.

David Hume insisted that, "What motivates us to right (and wrong) behavior . . . were our passions, and rather than being relegated to the margins of ethics and philosophy, the passions deserve central respect and consideration."[14] Hume also believed that moral distinctions are derived from passion rather than from reason. "Morals excite passions, and produce or prevent actions."[15] By contrast, reason is "perfectly inert" and can never produce or prevent an action. We do take a stand on the relationship between reason and passion later in the book. Although we do, like the philosopher Georg Hegal, affirm that **nothing that is great in the world has been accomplished without passion**. In like manner, the term "passions" appears in many historic works of poetry and history.[16]

More Recent Definitions

Although the use of the word passion to specifically represent a strong emotion or desire is first recorded around 1250 AD, "the generalized meaning of a strong liking, enthusiasm (as in a passion for horses) is first recorded in 1638."[17] The *Oxford English Dictionary* (updated in 2002) cited 12 different perspectives on the concept of passion, first presenting the use of the term representing the suffering of pain, specifically the suffering connected to Jesus' Crucifixion in Christian theology. Among these dictionary listings, the specific meanings that help build context are:

passion/noun (a) A strong barely controllable emotion; (b) A fit or outburst of such an emotion; (c) A literary composition or passage marked by strong emotion; an emotional speech. A strong enthusiasm for (specified) thing; an aim or object pursued with strong enthusiasm.

passion/verb: Excite or imbue with (a) passion. Express or be affected by passion or a strong emotion.[18]

Psychologist Nico Frijda saw passions as often extending to desires, thoughts, plans, and behaviors that *persist over time*. "They may lead to performing behaviors regardless of costs, external obstacles, and moral objections. These are the characteristics of passion in the more modern sense—the desires, behaviors, and thoughts that suggest urges with considerable force."[19] In like manner, and as introduced at the beginning of this little book, as a functional definition *we consider passion to indicate those desires, behaviors, and thoughts that suggest urges with considerable force.*

Into the Flow with Passion

The idea of flow is a familiar one. We watch the flow of water as it moves down a riverbed or fills our drinking glass. We feel the flow of air as a breeze plays with our hair, and our lungs move rhythmically in and out, in and out. We sense feelings of joy and sadness, calm and anger flowing through us. And, sometimes, since energy follows thought, we can perceive the thought of another without the hearing of words. Close your eyes for a moment and try to recall a time when you knew what someone was thinking without hearing the words. We all have that ability, although few of us exercise it.

Sometimes—since energy follows thought—we can perceive the thought of another without the hearing of words.

And so it is with life. There is a flow, a current, punctuated by our concept of time, within which thoughts and actions (events) occur. Much like falling in love, when an individual finds their flow, life is forever changed. Then, when other thoughts and actions are consistent with the flow, when we follow our passion, they expand and create a larger flow. Cindy refers to going with the flow as riding the river of emotion. In her words,

> *Riding the undulating River of Emotion*
> *Flowing downward into a collective ocean*
> *Rising above the energy fervor*
> *Becoming a distant observer.*
> *Seeking a reflective thought deliberation*
> *Rising to a higher conscious liberation.*

Thoughts and actions that are inconsistent with the flow, that is, heading upstream against the larger flow, like swimming against the tide, must be quite strong to make any headway, and can easily be overcome by the larger flow or swept to the side, out of the current. This description is consistent with the flow of energy in a probability field.

As can be recognized from the descriptions above, the flow state is enabled by the strong emotion of passion. In one model of flow, passion is identified as a major attribute to creating the power of flow.

> Flow is engendered by passion—passion for life, for knowledge, for a cause, for a relationship, for truth. Passion means caring deeply about something beyond ourselves. It means engaging with it at intense levels. It means letting go of self-protective caution to involve ourselves wholeheartedly with what we love.[20]

This passion "opens us up to a larger picture." It is the intensity of flow, the intense desire to be "active and engaged in the course of events" and the intense drive to know truth, "to answer the basic questions of existence: why we're here, what we're supposed to be doing, what it all means. Not satisfied with surface explanations, we use every moment as an opportunity to break through to something new, to learn. We fully engage with what comes our way."[21]

In a discussion of people skills, Daniel Goleman, the foundational author of *Emotional Intelligence*, cited focus and passion as important elements of achieving group flow. "The demands of meeting a great goal inherently provide focus; the rest of life can seem not just mundane, but trivial by comparison. For the duration, the details of life are on hold."[22] Passion, driving the intensity of flow, *elevates values and engages reality at all levels* in its search for "what it means to be alive."[23] This is also reflected in the spiritual context of passion, a spiritual freeflow **as a strong vehicle for awakening**[24] and energy that helps people *speak from the heart*, drawing out other people and engaging them.[25]

Thus, both as an individual and as a collective, passion acts as emotional super-fuel, propelling us into the flow of life to think and act in a focused domain of interest. *For a fulfilling life, we are asked to live our passion.*

The Power of Flow

The concept of flow is a powerful one. Charles Belitz and Meg Lundstrom identify passion as one of the nine attributes that create the power of flow.[26] Flow—as a concept described by Csikszentmihalyi in the early 1990s and the subject of considerable research and study since that time—is defined as "the state in which people are so involved in an activity that nothing else seems to matter; the experience itself is so enjoyable that people will do it even at great cost, for the sheer sake of doing it."[27] This is the *optimal experience*, described as "when a person's body or mind is stretched to its limits in a voluntary effort to accomplish something difficult and worthwhile."[28]

Using Csikszentmihalyi's concepts of flow, the eight conditions that combine to create the flow experience are: *Clear goals; quick feedback; a balance between opportunity and capacity; deepened concentration; being in the present; being in control; an altered sense of time;* and *the loss of ego.* Csikszentmihalyi called this common experience by the term "flow" because "so many people have used the analogy of being carried away by an outside force, of moving effortlessly with a current of energy, at the moments of highest enjoyment."[29]

In discussing the origins of flow, Csikszentmihaly found elements of the flow experience in a number of religions—Christianity, Buddhism and Taoism, for example. He then quoted the anthropologist Mel Konner, who when asked if every culture produced a religion, why every culture sought God, answered: "It's not God—they are seeking the rapture of life, to understand what it means to be alive."[30] As we previously introduced and is worth repeating here, Belitz and Lundstrom, two authors who focus on this flow state, say:

> Flow is engendered by passion—passion for life, for knowledge, for a cause, for a relationship, for truth. Passion means caring deeply about something beyond ourselves. It means engaging with it at intense levels. It means letting

go of self-protective caution to involve ourselves wholeheartedly with what we love.[31]

Yes! This passion "opens us up to a larger picture."[32] And it is the intensity of flow, the intense desire to be "active and engaged in the course of events" and the **intense drive to know truth**, "to answer the basic questions of existence: why we're here, what we're supposed to be doing, what it all means … [to] use every moment as an opportunity to break through to something new, to learn."[33]

> Flow is engendered by passion—passion for life, for knowledge, for a cause, for a relationship, for truth.

In a discussion of people skills, focus and passion were cited as an important element of achieving *group flow*. "The demands of meeting a great goal inherently provide focus; the rest of life can seem not just mundane, but trivial by comparison. For the duration, the details of life are on hold."[34]

The concept of duration is the recognition that passion is not a constant, that is, it rises and falls. This pattern was discovered in a research study of thought leaders that is detailed in Chapter VI. This is in part because the human—as a complex adaptive system—has many areas of life that demand conscious attention in the instant such that an area of passion will not always demand center focus. Yet, when that area emerges again into conscious awareness, it generally brings with it a renewed recognition of passion. In other words, passion can reside in the unconscious—from which place it may or may not have an effect on related decisions and actions, and whose effect, when it does occur, may or may not be consciously recognized by the individual. Thus, *recognizing and understanding our passions adds considerable value to our ability to make conscious choices.*

II: The Passion Model

Passion is an emergent phenomenon, which can be induced by external events and circumstances and internal inducers, which become part of a set of stimuli. This passion is both externally observed (emotions) and internally felt (feelings) in a variety of ways, and is also correlated to the larger aspects of self. Note that the definition of passion, the internal inducers, lists of elements externally observed and internally felt, and a list of correlates to the larger self are all developed from the characteristics of passion which emerge from the literature, many of which were shared in Chapter I. The emergent model is shown at the end of this chapter. It just makes sense to understand this word "passion" by exploring characteristics connected to it. So, take a quick look at the model itself, and let's briefly talk about these groupings.

Inducers can be defined as a set of stimuli that includes considerable variation across individuals and cultures. **External Events and Stimuli** (Inducers) are forever changing such that they are clearly situation dependent and context sensitive. **Internal Inducers** include morals, values, purpose beyond ourselves, goals and needs, and a deep longing to make a difference. As examples, in a research on passion connected to leadership (see Chapter VI), thought leaders in the field of Knowledge Management were asked "What about your field of work excites your passion?"[35] Examples of their response that are Internal Inducers included:

- The work is really worthy.
- It's value creation.
- Learning things that you feel are important and can contribute to the world.
- Seeing ideas light people's eyes up.
- Creating the context for ordinary people to discover the extraordinary ways that they can co-create innovation and actionable knowledge around the things they care about.

Characteristics related to the **Externally Observed** grouping include: joy; passionate commitment, action and a sense of urgency; leadership in terms of unleashing energy, building, freeing and growing; a passion to serve; and speaking from the heart and drawing out other people and engaging them. Examples of response from the thought leader research study included:

- Enabling conversations.
- To get people to build knowledge and get into situations where you create an environment for creativity and innovation.
- Simple things create unexpected outcomes thinking together
- Building tools that engage more of the whole person.
- Joy. Makes work easier and more enjoyable.

Characteristics related to the **Internally Felt** grouping include: promoting the greater good; doing the right things right; duty toward others; intersects with goals and needs; it is "precious", of higher interest, and great; optimism and confidence in the future; and demands attention. Examples of response from the thought leader research study in this grouping included:

- Helping people make good decisions ... getting people to sense beyond short-term decisions.
- Intellectually stimulating and challenging
- Value of knowledge and what it can do for society, for individuals, for interactions between individuals.
- Building organizations that perform well on a sustainable basis and where people actually have a sense of fulfillment that they're doing the right thing.
- From the knowledge perspective, a very optimistic view of the future.

Characteristics related to **Self Correlates**, which refers to the correlation of self to a larger picture, include: part of a larger picture; what it means to be alive; flow experience; spiritual awakening; and making one's life meaningful. Examples of response from the KMTL study in this grouping included:

- Transformative nature of work.
- New way to look at the world; actually gives you new lenses and ways to look at the world.
- Creates meaning. People fulfilling something worthwhile in their lives.

- There was a sense of suddenly being a participant in some incredibly rapidly evolving passionate ecologies, knowledge ecologies.
- Nourishment and cultivation of the future.

Because this construction is based on a biological model (see Chapter III), passion is considered in terms of an autopoetic system, that is, a system that evolves through continuous exchange and interaction with its internal and external environment (both adapting to and influencing its environment). In the framework, feedback loops have been drawn from externally observed elements to passion as well as from internally felt elements to passion, indicating that—as an autopoetic system—the things we feel and the ways we act influence ourselves as well as our environment.

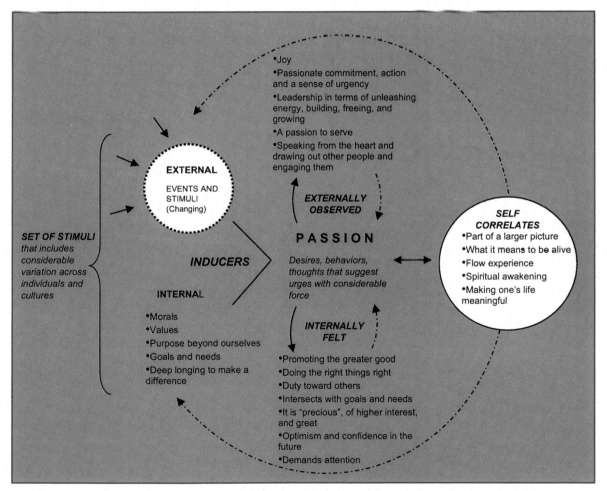

Framework to explore aspects of passion.[36]

There is also an arrow from the larger elements of Self Correlates leading to passion and then from passion back to Self Correlates, indicating that these elements have the quality of sustaining or increasing passion. This idea of larger elements of self-sustaining or increasing passion is based on the references shared in the previous chapter. For example, Kouzes and Posner asserted that the most passionate people are those who have a purpose beyond themselves; Melendez said effective leaders are passionate because of their commitment to the greater or public good; and Senge says that passions come from what you contribute, not what you get.

By now, you are forming your own opinions of which of your own experiences with passion form the foundation for what is most important in your life. Take a few minutes to bring those experiences to mind and reflect on each. For each experience, *Ask*: Did my passion play a positive or negative role in this experience? How did I feel about the experience after it was over? How do I feel about it now? Is this something I would like to experience again?

Assess your current passions. *Ask*: What are the things I am passionate about today? How do I feel when I think about these things? How do these passions relate to my dreams for the future?

From our unique viewpoint, we might think about life as a journey of passions, with those passions lighting the fires that move us forward into our dreams. We, of course, do have choice, but only if we first have awareness, and our passions help to bring that awareness of what we want out of life to the surface. And just maybe reading this little book can help us better understand our passions.

From our unique viewpoint, we might think about life as a journey of passions, with those passions lighting the fires that move us forward into our dreams.

III: The Wonder of Love

Love, considered the highest virtue on the emotional plane, early in life first develops through consciousness,[37] and is generally related by a growing child to the parent or caregiver. Later, the concept takes on different meanings, and during puberty this feeling of strong affection becomes attached to the idea of romance and sexual desire.

This strong affection also accompanies developing beliefs; for example, a growing connection to God. The highest form of this love—the love of God for man, and the love of man for God—is called agápē. This universal, unconditional love that transcends all things is derived from the ancient Greek word ἀγάπη, agápē, which translates as gaping, as with wonder and expectation, the mouth wide open.[38]

Love and freedom are irrevocably connected. In the Ageless Wisdom tradition, freedom is described as the first part of God's mind, and love as the second part.[39] This is because without the freedom to choose, love cannot come into being. This concept is critical to our understanding of love. *Love grows. It cannot be created, manufactured, or purchased. You cannot will or demand it.*

Without the freedom to choose, love cannot come into being. You cannot will or demand it.

As we are reminded:

The choice to function on the love-centered motivational frequencies, **where you are designed to function** [emphasis added], is the only choice that brings freedom. It does not limit you to a predetermined script but offers a range of behavior that evokes your fullest potential.[40]

Cindy has recognized that love is a flow. This is evident in her verse titled "Dream". The accompanying drawing is by artist Benjamin Mankin.

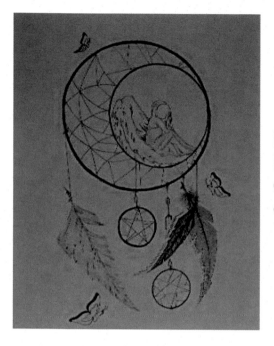

Let my dreams be guarded
Discovering pathways to new truths
Casting away all harm
Gathering forever flowing love.

Viktor Frankl, who endured three years at Auschwitz and other Nazi prisons, discovered the power of love in the midst of his suffering. The realization came as an image of his wife vividly arose in his mind. This is worth reading and learning from. As he describes:

A thought transfixed me: for the first time in my life I saw the truth as it is set into song by so many poets, proclaimed as the final wisdom by so many thinkers. The truth—that love is the ultimate and the highest goal to which man can aspire. Then I grasped the meaning of the greatest secret that human poetry and human thought and belief have to impart: *The salvation of man is through love and in love.* I understood how a man who has nothing left in this world still may know bliss, be it only for a brief moment, in the contemplation of his beloved. In a position of utter desolation, when many cannot express himself in positive action, when his only achievement may consist in enduring his sufferings in the right way—an honorable way—in such a position man can, through loving contemplation of the image he carries of his beloved, achieve fulfillment. For the first time in my life I was able to understand the meaning of the words, 'The angels are lost in perpetual contemplation of an infinite glory'.[41]

Love is the ultimate and the highest goal to which man can aspire ... the salvation of man is through love and in love.

-Victor Frankl

As a life of inflicted pain interrupted his connection, again and again, Frankl was able to find his way back from the prisoner's existence to this place of love. He did not know whether his wife was alive or not, but he did know one thing, that "Love goes very far beyond the physical person of the beloved. It finds its deepest meaning in his spiritual being, his inner self. Whether or not he is actually present, whether or not he is still at all, ceases somehow to be of importance."[42]

Love is born of understanding another, truly knowing another, looking within at their motives, sentiments and values. Once you really know who someone is, love is contagious. In *Urantia,* a recognized source in spiritual literature, it is suggested that each day or week we achieve an understanding of one or more individuals.

If each mortal could only become a focus of dynamic affection, this benign virus of love would soon pervade the sentimental emotion-stream of humanity to such an extent that all civilization would be encompassed by love, and that would be the realization of the brotherhood of man.[43]

In the young years of life—in the healthy family—love is often accepted as a given, with little reflection by young recipients whose focus is on discovery of the outside world from an "I" frame of reference. But as the teen years bring with them hormonal shifts—which we touch on later in Chapter IV—the discovery of love seems to be tied directly to relationships with others. We are learning about the deeper elements of life through the words and actions of others, and our own responses to those words and actions.

Here is an example from Alex's early writing:

How come when you growl, I can only smile
and a warmth spreads from my toes to my chin?
How come when I'm upset you always seem so calm,
and I listen?
How come your thoughts on MY problems
Always seem to ring so true?
How come you can say no and I like it?
How come your tones are able to sooth my fears and desires?
How come when I'm angry YOU laugh,
and I have to laugh too?
Who are you?

Perhaps surprisingly, the answer to that last question is "Through love, I am your teacher." Reflecting back over the years, how many people have emerged in different types of situations who have served for a while as our teachers, then moved on as life situations changed, with another teacher emerging and more life lessons to learn. And so many of these lessons reflect so many different expressions of love.

When the time is right, a teacher emerges in our lives, and so much of what is learned comes through different expressions of love.

The triangle of love theory[44] has three components: intimacy (emotional investment and closeness), passion (excitement and arousal) and commitment (relationship over time). While this model was applied specifically to romantic love, it has also been translated into more general terms, the idea of "feelings of affection, compassion, caring, and tenderness for others."[45]

For more than four years, Alex lived in Yokosuka, Japan. During this time she was Editor, then Editor-in-Chief of *The Seahawk*, the base weekly, and wrote for *Tokyo Weekender* and *Pacific Stars and Stripes*, who printed the base newspaper. U.S. Navy ships could only have short stays in port, so sailors were more often than not deployed during special days. So, Alex set about trying to figure out ways to help keep families connected. For example, for Valentine's Day, she would snap pictures and collect messages and print those throughout the weekly, which was delivered to the ships at sea. The following message in prose was printed at the center of one of these collages.

You're my friend.
My father, my mother,
my husband, my wife.
And far away,
not here today
with me.
Except inside ...
where
tiny little electric shocks
bubble down and around
when your name comes up.
Though you're far away
and not here today
with me.
And every day,
when you're away,
I live our life
as your daughter, son,
husband, wife.
And deep inside
my thoughts reach out
to keep you close.
Though you're far away
and not here today
with me.

I love you.

Love, like knowledge, expands when it is given away. When combined with wisdom, good things happen. For example, wise giving is the promotion of others to be giving, helping people find more ways to help others, which leads to beauty. Empathy comes into play in order to achieve wise giving. Empathy enables you to experience others in the sense of being them, with a whole new sense of reality emerging with the experience. As the understanding of others deepens, compassion emerges, then love. Unconditional love is an attribute of the advanced human that emerges as we progress on a continuum from sympathy to empathy to compassion, moving toward unconditional love.[46] We dive into this concept deeper in Chapter VII.

Cindy's verse called "Glimpses of Unconditional Love" captures the depth of passion as she reflects on her personal growth toward unconditional love. We share this verse from her collection titled *Painting the Reality of My Soul*.[47]

GLIMPSES OF UNCONDITIONAL LOVE

A parent holding a new born child
In a loving, caring arm.
Stopping to help a hurt animal,
Rendering it safe from harm.

Caring for someone you do not know,
From which you lovingly learn
To give to others without asking
For anything in return.

Helping others without them knowing
When sewing some new life seeds,
Doing what is best for everyone
Sometimes ignoring *your* needs.

Praying for someone that needs your prayers
Seeking not your glory known
Wisely giving as you live your life
Without showing seeds you've sown.

When doing for others, not keeping score
Just doing for doing's sake
And holding back the "I told you so"
When others make a mistake.

Reaching out with a calm helping hand
Whenever someone may fall
Understanding that the universe
Owes one's self nothing at all.

Have patience when others are learning
However slow and steady
Knowing that others will seek the truth
In time, when they are ready.

Think about the world all around us
And everything that we do.
There're Glimpses of Unconditional Love
Growing within me and you

Love Related to Cooperation and Collaboration

Cooperation and Collaboration are the highest virtues of the physical plane. An individual cannot expand without interaction with others. Along with gratitude, admiration and forgiveness, *love is a hive emotion that supports cooperation*, which leads to an edge in survival of a group. As demonstrated through history,

> A cooperative group will bring down a mastodon more readily than an asocial group. A cooperative group can form the "turtle" in battle; a Roman offensive formation that sacrifices the men on the outer flanks, but easily defeats a group of selfish-only soldiers. A cooperative group can create agriculture, towns, technology, and music (singing, marching, and laughing tunes the group). To the extent that cooperation and altruism have a genetic basis, this entire group will pass on its genes more readily than a group that lacks cooperation and altruism.[48]

You may have heard Darwin's meme "survival of the fittest." However, what most people *don't* know is that Darwin had discovered that this was not true. In a later book, *The Descent of Man*, Darwin pointed out that, "Those communities which included the greatest number of the most sympathetic members would flourish best and rear the greatest number of offspring."[49] Thus began the recognition that "cooperation and unity, rather than survival of the fittest, are the keys to the success of a species."[50] In fact, cooperation was identified as the key factor in evolution and survival![51] Little wonder that cooperation and collaboration are recognized as the highest virtue on the physical plane, although this can sometimes be difficult for humans.

Pretty much any word beginning with "co" requires elements of cooperation and collaboration to succeed. For example, some other "co" words that are used often are co-evolving, co-service, co-creating, and community. And no doubt you could add to this list!

Love in the Workplace

The phenomenon of love explicitly cultivated in the work environment has been seen as increasingly common in the current age.[52] In this context, love is often translated in terms of caring, sharing and supporting, and is tied to the human capability of empathy.

> In the context of organizations, love can be translated in terms of caring, sharing and supporting, and is tied to the human capability of empathy.

This is the second time empathy has come up, and it will come up again. Empathy has been called a hypothesis that humans make based on a combination of visceral, emotional and cognitive information, a "muddle of resonance, attunement, and sympathy."[53] We would add that there is an element of passion involved, a *subjective* deep caring for others. In contrast, there are other authors who feel that empathy is *objectively* trying to experience the inner life of another.[54] Perhaps both are right.

There are three different types of empathy: (1) a cognitive-based form called perspective-taking, that is, seeing the world through someone else's eyes (which is objective in nature); (2) literally feeling another's emotions, a *personal distress* caused by "emotional contagion" (which becomes heavily subjective in nature); and (3) recognition of another's emotional state and feeling in tune with it, what is called *empathic concern* (which is subjective in nature).[55]

Interestingly enough, from a neuroscience viewpoint, the physiological basis for empathy is so inherent in brain function that it has been extensively documented in scientific experiments with other tested primates. For example, in a study of rhesus monkeys when one monkey pulled a chain for food, a shock was given to that monkey's companion. The monkey who pulled the chain refused to pull it again for 12 days, that is, the primates would literally choose to starve themselves rather than inflict pain on their companions![56] Empathy appears to be *nature's lesson for a kinder society*.[57]

> Empathy—which in some forms can carry with it a passion for others—appears to be nature's lesson for a kinder society.

Although the neurobiology of empathy is still in its early development,[58] we do know that a key component of empathy is feeling. The insula—described as the limbic integration cortex lying beneath the temporal and frontal lobes—appears to "play an important role in both the experience of self and our ability to distinguish between ourselves and others."[59] Research has found that, beyond basic sensations, the insula mediates the extreme limits of emotions, ranging from severe pain to passionate love.[60]

Love has also been related to what is characterized as virtue-oriented communities,[61] which context is strongly tied to the community leader's virtue anchored by a personal motivation toward "good" and informed by character strengths. By a leader acting in love, that is, by listening to employees, communicating openly, exhibiting compassion, etc., others are inspired to do the same.[62] Leading by example starts the process toward a culture of love, then the energy of love itself continues the process. As one research study thought leader described:

> ... [Love] allows for an inner wealth, an insight, greater self-knowledge, self-confidence, and a great strength of character ... a very strong self-awareness. So I think it is not immediate, it is not only by example ... example leads people to think about love, to question themselves more, to be more aware.[63]

In some literature love is considered an organizational virtue. For example, one author describes love as "a habit that facilitates decision-making ... serves to evaluate actions ... and moves the will to act in a particular way."[64] That particular way *begins with ethics and is exhibited by honesty, kindness and care.*

Final Thoughts

Emotions are a gift to humanity which, when applied well, create great harmony and connect us in Oneness. However, when mismanaged or out of balance, emotions can create conflict, negativity and war. We've all had moments where our emotions seemed out of balance, and were difficult to manage. Yet, there is an aliveness to those feelings. Here's an early reflection from Alex.

Tears that flow unevenly down my face
And deepen the color on my cheeks as they dry,
And resultant itching that tightens the skin
And causes my hand to pump in response,
Stay yet awhile.

Life that fills my lungs with air and sights
And causes my hand to glide over this paper.
Hand that grasps this pen and urges it onward,
Mind that spurs my grief yet cries out,
Stay yet awhile.

Love that causes anguish and pulls my breast apart
And fills my soul with turmoil and concern.
He that holds my life and thoughts in his hand
And keeps my hopes from drowning in tears,
Stay yet awhile.

However, once we become masters of our emotional system, love and passion weave their way through all elements of our lives, guiding us toward intelligent activity and becoming more fully the co-creators of the life we choose to live.

IV: The Passions of the Body

In a biological context, passion is an emotion (externally observed) or feeling (internally experienced), a biologically-determined process that can be induced by internal or external events and circumstances. This induction process may be either conscious or subconscious to the individual. "The brain induces emotions from a small number of brain sites, most of them located below the cerebral cortex and are known as subcorticals."[65] Cognitive changes are induced through emotions via the secretion of certain chemicals that cause significant alterations in brain function. Such alterations may change the mode of cognitive processing, such as the sensitivity of auditory and visual sensors. Thus, we observe *very real physical shifts* along with our passionate thoughts and feelings.

The body itself can be a thing of joy. In this short prose, Alex captured a moment in the joyful discovery of the body.

Exhilaration!
I want to run, dance, smile!
An overwhelming fullness expands within my chest
And my cheek bones ache from grinning.
I twirl around with my arms crossed on my breasts
And my hands grasp opposite shoulders.
My feet kick and hop,
I bend at the waist to examine their behavior.

The sun's rays stream into my body.
They feel so warm and fresh and new.
I rub my hands over the flesh of my leg.
I am real.
I am alive!

Drawn from Cindy's verse, an example of chemical shifts that every healthy human being experiences early in life has very much to do with hormones.

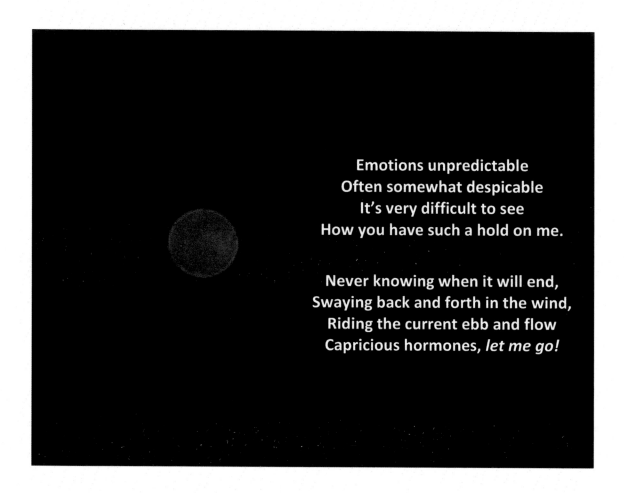

Emotions unpredictable
Often somewhat despicable
It's very difficult to see
How you have such a hold on me.

Never knowing when it will end,
Swaying back and forth in the wind,
Riding the current ebb and flow
Capricious hormones, *let me go!*

Damasio talked about a range of stimuli that constitute inducers for **certain classes of emotions**, allowing for a considerable variation in the type of stimuli that can induce an emotion (both across individuals and cultures). But all the stimuli are considered part of the set of inducers in our passion model.

In a more serious poetic treatment, Cindy addressed her raging hormonal reactions as a battle between spirit and the flesh, and this was written long before she had access to this same treatment by poets, novelists and philosophers alike. Here is an example.

SPIRIT AND THE FLESH

Have you ever wondered why, after a weak moment
You felt, "Come on now, I should have known?"
Why did you carry on that way with this life lesson?
You know how many times you've been shown.
Yet, you go and repeat the mistakes over again,
Wondering, "Is this the curse of man?"
For weakness in the flesh is a strength in the spirit,
Which is a truth I now understand.

Now, whenever you feel an inner turmoil coming
And the world seems to be upside down,
That's when you start pleading for needed peace to return,
For the drama to not come around.
Give serious thought to the concept that, just maybe,
The battle's happening inside of you
For when the spirit and the flesh war with each other
It brings havoc to all that we do.

When the flesh is weak and you're meandering around
In all the places you should not go
You are pulled in with an irresistible fervor,
Feeling high first, and then feeling low.
By the weakened flesh you are tempted while being drawn
To what your spirit knows is not right.
Unbeknownst to you, the spirit and flesh are at war
In a perpetual everlasting fight!

Meanwhile, as Cindy moved in and out of relationships, searching for something not understood, these same yearnings were traveling through the mind and body of a young Alex. She did not name her prose, but rather wrote and scribbled—on scraps of paper, the inner flaps of books, along the edges of church bulletins and in the folds of her mind. Perhaps this prose brings up some of your own memories of those early years?

> I am about the yearning of you,
> Wishing to be held tightly against your chest,
> My face pushed gently into your neck.
> I am about the wanting of you,
> Your heat calming my timorous body,
> Your strength filling my voids.
>
> I am about the needing of you,
> Asking you the questions that sear my mind,
> Comforted by the strength of your will.
> I am about the loving of you,
> Craving the warmth of your inner soul,
> Fulfilling the longings of my own.

But the encounters of the body were not always framed in such a positive fashion. This prose from Alex's early 30's seems to share a different story.

Three small spots rest on the soft flesh of my upper arm.
They are lighter yet than yesterday.
For yesterday I could catch their color
As my arm rose and fell upon the waves
The swirling salt water caressed the skin
As its sensitive surface generated warmth, then cold,
Corresponding to the changing undercurrents.

The ocean! Wild and free and calling to me.
Gurgling fish bubbles rising to my right,
Water-logged kept entangling my left arm.
And those spots! I can hardly see them now.
But they are there. They must still be there.
Yesterday they were there!

I lay drying in the sun,
Feeling the refreshing warmth upon my skin,
My eyes creating rainbows on the inside of thin lids.
A sand gnat tickles my right thigh.
I ignore the non-unpleasant sensation and continue dreaming
Until the gnat moves upward and must be slapped.

I crack my lids to assure an accurate mark
And watch as three added spots pass with my arm.
They ARE there.
Three dots the size of a thumb and two fingers.
Your thumb and two fingers.
They ARE there.

But today they are fading, only slightly discolored.
One is intertwined with a freckle
And they can hardly be told apart.
Almost as I watch they seem to disappear, not quite, but almost.
For today they are still real,
And you are still real. Tomorrow?

The five human senses of form—seeing, hearing, smelling, tasting and touching—offer the opportunity to engage fully and passionately in the everyday experiences of life. There was a segment of writing in Alex's life that focused largely on exploring these senses and, specifically, of pulling the reader into the experience. For example, while living in Japan and writing for the *Tokyo Weekender*, Alex penned a front-page piece titled "Choo-choo: Yokosuka to Tokyo." We're going to include a few of Alex's photographs that accompanied the article.

CLICK, CLACK, CLANK, STOMP, STOMP (slow and steady). SHUFFLE, SHUFFLE (lighter). A distant hum of cars.

The chatter of voices dominates a long, airy whistle; the voices in turn subdued by the building drum and hiss of an approaching train.

CLICK, CLACK, CLANK (stronger, faster now); heels rapidly move up concrete stairs. A woman's voice echoes over the P.A. system; a layered voice, soft and round. CLOMP, CLOMP, SHUFFLE, SHUFFLE, CLACK, CLACK.

Nearby a muffled cough is followed by the intake of congested breath. As a young man sways to and fro, the soft hint of a rock beat leaks through is Walkman headset.

A loud roar, the swish of air, a hiss. Bodies crush through opened doors. HISS. Instant motion; pressure. HISS. An echo comes with temporary darkness.

SQUEAK, SQUEAK; passengers swing with the rhythm of the train.

The scrape of bodies and packages, pocketbooks and briefcases. The rustle of a turning news page. The more regular, simple flip of al book page. And always the voices, occasionally punctuated with the clearer sound to my ears of an English word.

SSSSSSS; the next stop is reached, more sensed by the feet than heard. The door slides open, a warning whistle races in. A drift of (fresh?) air and then the intake of breath as still more bodies crush together. Grunts. Silent grimaces of discomfort; the quieter pressed lips of tolerance.

CLACKETY, CLICK; WHEELS AGAINST TRACK. One briefcase slips; a helping hand keeps it from falling. "Gracias" comes the reply. (Now, where did **that** come from?)

A distant P.A., the click of closing doors, a swoosh of air, and CLICKETY, CLACK. From the top of the car, the purr of rotating air.

A siren in the distance interrupts the regular/irregular sounds as the train files toward the hub of Japan.

The squeak of plastic against leather, leather against metal. Up, up, the cream-colored, muted reflections of reality on top of the car motion sway in slow motion. The whir of the fan as it makes its round, with difficulty now. Always the soft murmur of voices.

Through the windows, green splotched with brown and gray, green and concrete, lines darkness. Darker grays dotted and streaked with yellow-golds and faded whites.

Yokohama. The press of mankind. Blessed by the person afeared of close places. Through the close air the smell of Vitalis, winging the memories of youth.

TAP, TAP. The grate of fingernails against (plastic?) A young woman struggles to keep hold of her black "Cherry" color slide file. The smooth silver handrail of the seat below stops the file's downward path. She quickily recovers it.

And the train passes:

. . . people.

. . . houses. Just houses, you say? No. Flashing dots of orange and gray, dark and medium blues, browns, greens and rust. And atop each, the slim shiver of a towering antenna.

Lines of black fly through the air, following alongside, paralleling the train's progress towards the inner city. The lines are stretched tightly between shafts of brown, weatherworn wood, barely glimpsed as the speed picks up.

And sticks, smaller, slimmer. Graves, huddled together in the midst of the living.

A red brick walkway and dull, still green/brown water. The blue of a station. A field of blue stolen by a bulleting training heading away from the city. A green and orange training momentarily paces at a distance. A flash of white/cream from the other direction blocks out the green and orange. It is gone, blended into the constant pass of houses.

Just house, you say? No. Structures, many conforming in size, but decorated with waving towels and bedding, shirts and pants, personalized …

Tracks. So tightly interwoven. Who's going where? They cross each other, then run away, then come back together.

The green and orange again in the distance. Then a bank of green obscures the view. Gray poles (a surprisingly empty station!) ... but, then, everyone's already on this train.

Apartment structure replace the houses. Another stream of green/brown water followed by the dotted white-against-brown of a baseball team. Practicing? The orange and yellow twists of a playground.

Gray walkways streaked with pink in chorus with large office buildings.

Inside, hands grip plastic rings tightly; many eyes are closed.

And outside, signs ... in every color, every shape, every size, filled with ... assorted squiggles.

CLICKETY, CLANK, SQUEAK. Tokyo is near. But on board, the crunched segment of humanity has fallen asleep.

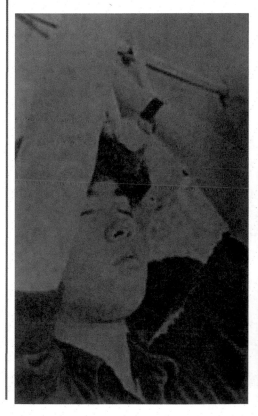

There are seven primary energy centers, or chakras, located in the electromagnetic field that is connected to the physical body, and many, many smaller chakras that facilitate the flow of our life energy, which has many names, but which we will refer to as *Ki*. Each primary energy center is unique, having connections to one or more of the seven senses used to process incoming energies, and connecting to various organs of the body in terms of their functionality and health. The seven senses referred to include the five senses of form and the two expanded senses—from the heart our connection to others, and from the top of our heads the connection to the larger ecosystem, whether you consider that a Quantum field, a consciousness field or a God field.

It is the flow of *Ki* that gives life cohesiveness, allowing different centers to communicate with each other and integrate into a single life. If there is not enough *Ki* flowing through the centers, the senses cannot communicate with each other and the body begins to fail. As you can see, all of our senses contribute to a healthy body—which supports a healthy and happy life.

As an example, the throat energy center, long associated with communication and providing a sense of others and how to speak to others, is also associated with our sense of taste, which is both a comparative sense and a discriminating and discerning sense. As Alex describes:

On that Sunday afternoon when the Sun finally melted the cold,
Midst the slowly waning death spiral of a global epidemic,
Claustrophobic feelings were dissuaded by smells filling the household
And saliva wetting the tastebuds tossed aside the raging pandemic.

There's nothing quite like the memories of hot cinnamon apple pie
To distract—or perhaps totally abscond with—our negative thought,
Except maybe the actual tasting and swallowing to satisfy
The yearning of the heart, and hunger for deeper meaning that it's brought.

Quite simply, we as humans have this amazing, special sense of taste
That can help us cleanse the palette of life, and put everything in place.

V: The Passions of the Head

To help understand the meaning of intellectual passions, we look to a research study done with chimpanzees where the researcher demonstrated that chimpanzees "derive pleasure from the discovery of a new ingenious manipulation, quite apart from the practical benefit they derive from it . . . they will repeat the performance for its own sake, as a kind of play."[66] Polanyi likened these intellectual tastes of the animal to those of a child, and said that these "prefigure, no doubt, the joys of discovery which our articulate powers can attain for man."[67] Polanyi went on to identify *science itself* as an intellectual passion.

> Passions charge objects with emotions, making them repulsive or attractive; positive passions affirm that something is precious. The excitement of the scientist making a discovery is an intellectual passion, telling that something is intellectually precious ... The function which I attribute here to scientific passion is that of distinguishing between demonstrable facts which are of scientific interest, and those which are not . . . scientific passion serves . . . as a guide in the assessment of what is of higher and what of lesser interest; what is great in science, and what is relatively slight.[68]

Alex easily recognizes the intellectual passion of science. Her partner David is a nuclear physicist and mathematician, who also, along with other degrees, achieved a PhD focused on neuroscience and learning. Over a ten-year period, Alex collaborated with David as he developed an expanded model of experiential learning based on new discoveries in neuroscience, and the reality is that she learned more than she did with her own PhD studies! And all of that learning weaves through everything they research and everything they write. Indeed, science is an intellectual passion.

Several points in Polanyi's work are significant to our discussion of passion. First, his **close linking of joy with intellectual passion**. Second, his assertion that positive passions affirm that something is precious. Third, that passion can be used as a determinant of what is of higher interest and great. In other words, he confirms that in our discovery of self, those things that incite passion within us provide an indicator of what is really important to us, what we really care about. Thus, the emergence of the expression: *Follow your passion.*

Writing as Passion

Writing itself can be considered a passion of the head, requiring a certitude while interjecting elements of the heart and spirit, and executed through the body. There is an intrinsic quality to this passion. Cindy calls this a "flooding of the senses from all directions." That passion is clear in her poem "All Becomes One Becomes All."

Journey through my lives of what came before,
Reaching far back to see my reflections.
Musty flowers fill the air about me
Flooding my senses from all directions.

Floating and weaving and drifting through time
As a familiar fragrance fills the air.
Focused, still wondering where I came from,
Going further back through time if I dare.

Lanky personage in a dreamlike state
Above a lifeless planet, just drifting.
Light violet face with metallic-like suit;
Turning of day to darkness is shifting.

Splitting cracks tear the metallic body,
Streaming out a bright pulsating white light.
All is escaping that's contained within
Under the night sky, with tiny stars bright.

Body floating within the atmosphere
While the light from within escapes its wall.
All beings contained in the light are one;
In the radiance I 'm one with the all.

Coming back with many faces showing,
All nationalities, cradle to tomb,
Trailing quickly across the universe
Entering back in, through my mother's womb.

Arriving back to the place I began,
And meditating on what I recall,
A guided impartation entered in:
"The all will be one and one will be all."

Writing from the head but with passion, Alex played a central role in a story written more than 30 years ago called "Renewal." Couched in a fictional context, all the emotions of this life event punctuate the writing, enabling a release of much that had been held within.

Renewal

He began at the back, scanning each headline for context and applicability before carefully sliding the next page across his lap to continue his search. He found it in the middle of C10: an unbolded, 16-point Helvetica head stating, "Emotions linked to Vitamin A". An incorrect, no, imprecise headline. Sixteen points worth of negation for two-years-worth of exacting research.

His eyes glided down the two short columns below the head, noting the explication, hovering closer to reality, which linked the lack of vitamin A to emotional instability. He also noted the misspelling of his name.

The core of his research, of course, lay far beyond the capability of newspaper reporting. Even al bold, 36-point banner across the top of page one would lack correct emphasis for the depth of his study. His work proved beyond doubt, and his Thomas-methodology was unapproachable, that man could achieve complete control of his emotions through vitamin infusion, of which Vitamin A was but one proponent. What his research did *not* prove, but of which he was cognizant, was that control of emotions, in equal proportion with stimulated mental activity, precipitated control of environment.

He closed the paper, carefully avoiding unnecessary handling of heavy newsprint areas, and placed it evenly on the nook table. The nook was indeed *off* the kitchen, but not *in* the kitchen. Therefore, the table situated within the nook was a nook table. He did not own a kitchen table.

He rose, still smiling, and poured fresh coffee into his half-filled mug, leaving a leeway of 1.2 centimeter between the streaming liquid and the top of the mug. He brought the edge of the sugar bowl over his mug and transferred 1 ¼ teaspoon of the sweetener into the coffee, executing three swishes with his measuring utility before delegating it to the dishwasher.

Returning to his chair, he sipped the dark liquid, then placed the mug, to void the possibility of spillage, in the approximate center of his nook table. With fluidity, and unwasted motion, he leaned slightly to the right as his hand glided down to the remaining sections of newspaper piled neatly on the floor. His fingers flicked through the tops of the folded section, fanning the stack to facilitate ease of future accessibility.

Sliding the Style section from its place in the stack, he adjusted the remaining sections proportionately to compensate for the removal. His efforts rewarded, he straightened in his chair, opening the section to B11.

His eyebrows flicked with anticipation as he focused in on "Dear Abby". This flicking of the eyebrows was an allowed response, situated equally with the slight smile or frown in acceptable normalcy patterns of responsive human behavior. Superficial responses, these, not rooted to the deeper tides of uncontrolled human emotion. Allowed. And allowing him to remain an unburdened humanitarian, participating without shuffling through emotional overload.

"Dear Abby" encompassed three columns: two at 61 picas each and one at 82 picas, for a total of 204 picas of 9-point type set in columns 14-picas wide. The format, thought no necessarily the length, differed from Abby's normal style: the first paragraph, set in boldface, was from Abby, followed by a letter the columnist must have felt warranted printing in full. He scanned Abby's words. She sympathized with the writer, noting this was a "frightening situation that could happen to anyone." Abby's value judgments proved almost as entertaining as her constituent's letters.

Leaning against the back of his chair, he crossed his legs, settling into the seat. The letter in Abby's column began "Dear John", a noted departure from "Dear Abby". Interest piqued, he read on.

Please go away. I didn't ask for your help.

I was upset. Stranded and alone way out Route 50 towards Middleburg. At least I made it to 50. Eight miles away, on a back, winding, barely-wide-enough-for-one-but-two-lane road is where it started. Or maybe it started earlier when the brakes on my brother's car failed, so after working Saturday morning he couldn't drive his car out to join the father-son camping trip underway. So, I drove him out in my car; it's my son he plays father for, so I drove him out. Only it was dark when we finally found the campsite, and frightening driving back towards home through unknown territory.

Still, it would have been okay. I'm a good driver. Good reflexes avoided the head-on collision that could have occurred as I slowly rounded an unknown bend in the road. That car must have been doing 60 right down the middle of the road! But I'll be honest, his last-minute swerve helped, too. We didn't hit. Only I went off the road and there was a drop of some three feet to the right. The bottom of my car dragged about ten feet, then the front right tire hit something (my camping son later said he thought it must have been one of those dead trees along the way), and the car bounced back up on the road, twirling with the effort. Still, I was okay.

The other car didn't bother to stop. Neither did a second car coming along behind me. The people inside looked, but the car didn't stop. And then there was nothing but darkness. I cried for five minutes, then, pulling together my temporarily-misplaced inner strength, checked the right side of the car (which in the darkness appeared wet, but normal) and slowly continued my route home.

He paused to reach toward his mug, easing his hand around the base, and slowly brought the now-warm liquid to his lips. After downing several swallows, he returned the mug to its former location, and returned to the Dear Abby column.

I made it back to Route 50 before the thud, whack of my rear tire became unbearable. "Hold, dear rim," I whispered, swinging the car left and searching the roadside for some sign of help. There were other cars on the road now, most of them interested in getting around my slow-moving, crippled vehicle. But still, there was no place to sop. Trees, an occasional house off in the distance, more trees, an intersecting road, until … finally … a Chevron sign to the right? "Thank you," escaped as I turned right and creaked the twenty feet to the lit structure. Only it was closed. There was a big sign in the bright-lit window. Closed.

Still, there were several lit telephone booths fifteen feet away, to the right. "It's okay," I breathed as I ran past the air-purged right rear tie, which had nevertheless brought me to safety, and headed towards the phones. In a matter of seconds, I had AAA on the phone, trying desperately to describe *exactly* where I was.

He uncrossed his legs and straightened in the chair, pulling the folds out of the paper. Something of interest was going to happen. You could tell with Dear Abby, emotions printed rampant right over the column breaks. He returned to the newspaper, digressing to the last paragraph indent.

That's when you hand touched my shoulder. "Excuse me, Miss, I'll fix it," you said. Still on the phone, I explained I had AAA on the way out, only you smiled and said, "I'll take care of you" and continued over to my car.

Over the next fifteen minutes, you did change the tire. Only, in the midst of the changing, you walked back over to where I stood on the phone. Bending near my left hand you speculated, "Married? Where's your husband?"

I have no husband. Hesitantly, I lied, "He should be here," to which you replied, with that same smile, "But he's not. Too bad for him, but good for me." Ice. Down, down, spreading inside out. "No!" shouted silently through my head.

But I stayed on the phone, and the now-several ladies on the AAA end of the phone helped. They'd heard your words. They guessed your intent. They coached me through bouts of feigned anger, a request to talk to their supervisor, questions about just how close was the AAA truck now. And through all this, you told me over and over that everything was okay, "Just hang up the phone, lady." And, putting on your jacket, "I'm cold. I don't like to be cold, I like to be warm. Do you like to be warm?"

A preemptory shiver passed through his stiffened shoulders. Now here was a perfect example of uncontrolled emotion. Not his shiver. Though departing slightly from his behavior patterns, the slight muscle response of a shiver, twitching per se, did not warrant serious contemplation. External chilling from internal stimuli did.

Still, I talked on the phone, talked about the imminent arrival of the tow truck, thanking you for your help and saying you could leave because the truck was right around the corner. AAA was going to check the car out, anyway. You told me your name was John. I didn't want to know you name. And then you left. You pulled up to Routh 50, turned left, and disappeared.

Relief. "He's gone," into the phone. And then I left the phone line open wile I went to make sure the car would run. Grabbing my purse, I searched around for the keys, only, two headlights flashed towards me. I dropped my purse and ran back to the phone. "He's back," I whispered and then stated loudly into the phone. "The car seems fine. I really don't know why you insist on checking it out." You walked to the phone next to me and made a call. Then, commented to me that I should just hang up and forget AAA. Only I couldn't. That telephone had become my lifeline.

You hopped back into your van, drove around the lot twice, and then returned to the phone for a second telephone call, still murmuring for me to hang up the phone. Shaking, I yelled into the phone, "It's about time! I'm glad you finally found me?" And you left, quickly, turning on Route 50, this time to the right.

"He's gone again," I cried into the phone. And then the police car pulled into the station. Finally, finally, I was found. And everything was okay, only, the ice melts slowly. So slowly. Prickly fear stretching in and down when I think, when I dream ...

Please. Please go away.

Abby had not printed the writer's name, either out of compassion or in consideration of column length. Nor had she (intelligently, he noted) taken the opportunity to philosophize further.

He allowed his face to register a light smile, which a casual observer would credit to warmth and sympathy, as he carefully repeated the sequence of paragraph four. Then, he rose, lifted the still-more-than-half-full mug from the nook table, and, pouring the cold, dark liquid down the kitchen drain, deposited the mug in the dishwasher and rinsed the remnants of coffee from the sink.

Walking briskly to the front room, he sorted through the mail propped between two brass dolphins atop his oak, rolltop desk. Two bills, six advertisements (five with coupons), his license renewal notice, and a birthday card from his mother, which she insisted on addressing childishly as "Jonnie" rather than "John", which was his name. He put the bills in his briefcase, placed the renewal notice in the desk, pulled the coupons, and deposited the remainder in the trash. Donning his tweed jacket and cashmere overcoat, he picked up his briefcase and walked out of the apartment, locking the door behind him, heading into the new day.

On January 31, while standing in line at the Express Office of the Department of Motor Vehicles, they met. Again.

Note that in this story, while the writing is performed with passion—with a strength that can be felt—a primary emotion that is explored throughout this writing is fear. Is it fear that motivates the victim of our story? This begs the question: Is fear a passion? No, we think not. Fear (of loss, failure, the unknown, not being good enough) holds you back, confuses your decision-making, either making it difficult to move forward OR, from our primal instincts, triggering a fight or flight response. And when you do make a decision or take an action out of fear, the results bring with them negative feelings such as resentment, helplessness, frustration or inadequacy.

Conversely, passion urges you forward, toward something (not away from something), making you feel alive and centered. I remember an adage my father repeated again and again. "In all things in life, run toward, not away from." The way I interpreted that was to always run toward that which you want, not away from your problems, and I've tried to do that in my life. With passion, there's an energy and willingness, even eagerness, to get something done, to go after something, and an excitement in the experience. Hmmm ... that's certainly true when thinking about Descartes primary passions of the soul in terms of their positive affects—wonder, love, desire and joy. Is that true also for hatred and sadness?

> As Alex's father repeatedly emphasized to her: *In all things in life, run toward, not away from.*

While both Alex and Cindy have always tried to distance themselves from ANY feeling of hatred, sometimes that word surfaces in their heads, not so much aimed at a person, but rather aimed at some situation each was in, or event or action that occurred: "I hate when that happens" or even, "I hate feeling this way." OK, when reflecting upon it, yes, there is certainly power in hate to affect your decision-making and move you to respond OR move you to NOT respond, which actually IS a response.

In contrast, sadness can certainly cause one to sink into a state of being versus urging forward an action. While René Descartes considered sadness one of the primary passions of the soul, if it was left unchecked, he also recognized that it could slide into melancholy, which caused a *corruption of passions.*[69] So, there appears to be a range where, balanced with reason, passion accelerates growth to a point where it can take over, perhaps better described as an "obsession" than a passion.

The author or co-author of hundreds of stories, articles and books, Alex suggests that as she focused her attention on each area and plunged into the writing, her passion for and excitement about the project at hand expanded. Thus, she suggests that we move in and out of passion, dependent upon where our intention is set and attention is focused, a pattern we've already run into and is further discussed in Chapter VI. There is a small Conscious Look Book in the *Possibilities that are YOU!* (Volume 6) on attention and intention.

This movement is consistent with psychological concepts related to the wants and desires of humans coupled with a continuous, whether conscious or unconscious, hunger for change. Think about something you really wanted in your life, something that took a large amount of time and effort to achieve; for example, buying a new car, learning a new skill, or getting a college degree. You save and save, practice and practice, or study and study to achieve your goal, and finally you DO achieve it! Congratulations! Feels pretty good. Only, once you have it, somehow, it's not as important. And pretty soon there is something else on the horizon that catches your attention, and the cycle begins again.

There are several lessons to be learned from this process. First is that focusing attention helps achieve intention. Second, that when we achieve a goal over time that goal loses importance in terms of our attention, and something new takes its place. This is who we are! People are verbs, not nouns. This is not surprising since to live is to be in a continuous process of change. Our bodies have 50 trillion cells continuously changing. Nothing about us is static, and it never has been. We pulse with change: absorbing food, processing air, dividing cells, making and pushing our secretions, transmitting electrical signals.

> People are verbs, not nouns. Our bodies have 50 trillion cells continuously changing. Nothing about us is static, and it never has been.

There are thousands of books and articles published on change—and change books take up several shelves in the Mountain Quest library—and, no doubt, there are millions of poems! Here is a verse titled "Change, Patience and Truth" with an accompanying drawing by artist Benjamin Mankin. With short and simple statements, Cindy captures and conveys a depth of thought on the character of the human journey.

A transfigured soldier named Change
Bends with the wind
While the turbulent storm is swirling fast.

A spirit warrior called Patience
Stands still knowing,
Before long, turmoil will be in the past.

An awaiting archer deemed Truth
When time is right,
Will innovate veracity at last.

Passion serves as a driver of focusing our minds, hearts, bodies and spirits based very much on choice, that is, emerging in support of that which is of higher interest to each individual, that upon which you focus your attention. We are indeed creators of our reality, creating our life story. As Cindy shares in her verse "Rhythms of Reality":

Ideas flowing in many rhythmic patterns
Connecting what was with what's to come
Gathering, storing new truths along the way
While holding on to where we came from.

The pulsing cadence of the biorhythm
Ever moving, ever growing thus
Each pattern spawning a new reality
Creating the life story of us.

Ah, and there we have the essence of it … we are creating a story, a story in which we can choose to play whichever role (in the moment) we are attracted to, and head whatever direction our passion leads us. And the reality is, this is a story which exists only in your mind! Tying our life together into a coherent story is one of the main jobs of consciousness![70]

> [J]ust as the novelist is selective with respect to character development, plot, etc., so the person who seeks the connective threads in the history of his life … has singled out and accentuated the moments which he experiences as significant, others he has allowed to sink into forgetfulness … The finished product is the 'fictionalized' history of a life, neither a lie nor 'the truth,' but instead a work of imagination, evaluation and memory.[71]

Evolution created the mind/brain to ensure survival through its meaning-making capacity, not just its memory! We tend to remember things that have meaning. The narrative language and connective tissue of stories communicates the nature and shape and behavior of complex adaptive phenomena. This is because stories capture the "essence of living things, which are quintessentially complex phenomena, with multiple variables, unpredictable phase changes, and all of the characteristics that the mathematics of complexity has only recently begun to describe."[72]

One researcher goes so far as to measure intelligence in terms of the number of stories an individual has to tell, and in terms of the size of an individual's indexing and retrieval schema that provide a mechanism for determining what is relevant to current experiences, and the ability to search and find that which is relevant to the story you are in.[73] Even simple stories have the capacity to convey or highlight intricate patterns, which can be used to explore situations hard to express out loud, to release unwanted patterns, to open our minds to new ways of thinking, and to create new futures.[74] So—whether in your mind, your heart, or on paper—write your story!

Passion and Reason

In *How the Mind Works*, Steven Pinker presented a theory that passions are "no vestige of an animal past, no wellspring of creativity, no enemy of the intellect" but that the intellect is "designed to relinquish control to the passions so that they may serve as guarantors of its offers, promises, and threats."[75] To illustrate, Pinker presented examples from *The Maltese Falcon*, *The Godfather*, *Dr. Strangelove* and other movies that demonstrate sacrifices of will and reason as effective tactics in the bargains, promises, and threats that are part of social relations. In *The Maltese Falcon*, the character played by Humphrey Bogart dares the henchmen to kill him, knowing he is needed alive in order for them to retrieve the falcon. The Godfather tells the heads of other crime families that he is a superstitious man, that if an unlucky accident befalls his son, he will blame them. Dr. Strangelove, a top nuclear strategist, carries the news that the doomsday machine is triggered automatically and cannot be reversed. These, then, are acting as guarantors.

In like manner, if you were buying a car from (for example) Mother Teresa, her passion and reputation for doing good would serve as the guarantor that you were not being cheated. Pinker concluded that "the apparent firewall between passion and reason is not an ineluctable part of the architecture of the brain; it has been programmed in deliberately, because only if the passions are in control can they be credible guarantors."[76] This certainly requires some thought!

The latest scientific findings reviewed by Norman Rosenthal suggest that we "endorse the existence of unconscious emotional processes and their powerful influence on preferences and actions."[77] While he admits emotions do not always work as they should, Rosenthal argues in favor of the **emotions as intelligent and necessary for proper decision-making**. He stated,

It is clear now that the two great domains, reason and passion, are both critical to our ability to make proper decisions. Emotion unchecked by reason can lead to disaster, but without emotion, a person is unable to plan properly or form and sustain social bonds, even in the presence of adequate reasoning ability … When passion and reason work well together, like the partners in a successful marriage, the outcome is a happy one. When they are at war, like hostile spouses, the result is no end of grief."[78]

Citing recent studies in neuropsychology, Damasio reported that human beings actually **require emotions in order to reason effectively**.[79] Similarly, Marinoff reminds us that, "People are not machines, nor should we behave like machines."[80] Cindy's verse titled "Balancing the Heart and Mind" (on page 49) explores this relationship.

Alex and Cindy agree on this point. Emotions and feelings provide the fodder for reasoning and judging, unique human capabilities that our very survival is dependent upon. In their research and resulting publications, Alex and her partner David focus on achieving intelligent activity through wisdom, which emerges from developing mental faculties with increasingly higher order patterns *coupled* with increasingly deeper connections with others. Intelligent activity is defined as *a state of interaction where intent, purpose, direction, values and expected outcomes are clearly understood and communicated among all parties, reflecting wisdom and achieving a higher truth.*

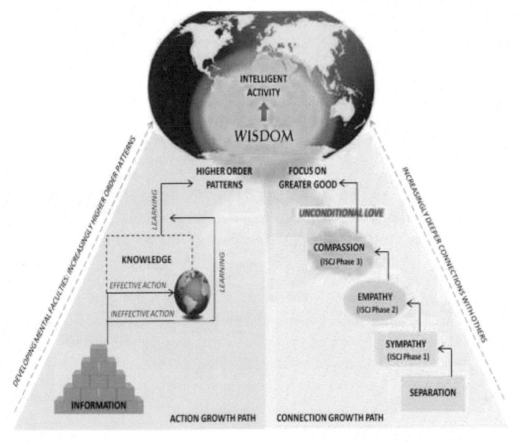

Emotions and feelings provide the fodder for reasoning and judging, unique human capabilities that our very survival is dependent upon.

In moving toward wisdom, the action growth path—developing mental faculties—builds on information, then knowledge as we act on that information with some level of effectiveness, with learning and the development of higher order patterns moving us closer to wisdom. The connection growth path—developing increasingly deeper connections with others—begins from the perception of separation and moves through feeling sympathy to empathy to compassion towards unconditional love, with a focus on the greater good. Thus, wisdom, which leads to intelligent activity, is very much inclusive of emotion. That model[81] appears on the bottom of the previous page.

Wisdom—the highest part of mental thought—emerges from a passion for living and learning. Representing *completeness and wholeness of thought*, wisdom is universally a lofty consideration, and too often we sense that it eludes us. The more we seek it, the more we understand that it comes through experiencing and learning, and brings with it the desire to learn more.

Wisdom occurs when activity matches the choices that are made and structured concepts are intelligently acted upon, thus directly connecting wisdom to intelligent activity, as shown in our model. The way this is described in *Urantia* is:

> Knowledge can be had by education, but wisdom, which is indispensable to true culture, can be secured only through experience and by men and women who are innately intelligent. Such a people are able to learn from experience; they may become truly wise.[82]

Looking through the combined lens of the body, mind and soul—and the emotions—Cindy explores the experiential and learning nature of life and how to achieve a balance that facilitates conscious expansion in the temporary state in which we now exist. Here are her words:

How does one balance the emotional heart
With the logical intellect mind?
Between passion and mind the harmony flow
Is not always easy to find.

For I physically hang out in a body
of brief temporal carnality
While I'm peering into the peculiar realm
of my spiritual reality.

Armed with the various learned lessons of self
With awareness of where I've come from;
Helps me discern the tribulations of life
And those I have yet to overcome.

Now I physically hang out in a body
of brief temporal carnality
While I'm peering into the peculiar realm
of my spiritual reality.

Somewhere along the way there's understanding
Of the path down which I am going;
Narrowing my focus so I can expedite
My conscious spiritual growing.

Still, I physically hang out in a body
of brief temporal carnality
While I'm peering into the peculiar realm
of my spiritual reality.

Passion and Creativity

In the Public Broadcasting Station (PBS) television series on "The Creative Spirit," Daniel Goleman, Paul Kaufman and Michael Ray revealed what they called the hidden anatomy of the creative process. They stated: "Finally, the element that really cooks the creative stew is passion. The psychological term is *intrinsic motivation*, the urge to do something for the sheer pleasure of doing it rather than for any prize or compensation."[83]

The Nobel Prize-winning physicist T. Amabile, when asked what he thought made a difference between creative and uncreative scientists, stated that the most successful, groundbreaking scientists were not always the most gifted ones, but those that were driven. "To some degree a strong passion can make up for a lack of raw talent. Passion 'is like the fire underneath the soup pot,' Amabile says. 'It really heats everything up, blends the flavors, and makes those spices mix with the basic ingredients to produce something that tastes wonderful'."[84]

Cindy agrees, reminding us in her verse that the passions of the past combine with our future aspirations to prepare us for the creative leap.

The past is recalled points in time gone by
The future is the unforeseen to come
In our mind the now puts them together
Then, what was, what's to come and now are one.

If yesterday affects my thoughts today
Future aspirations affect my paths
If now is a combination of both
Then past, present and future become one.

If a few seconds ago was the past
Before this thought's complete is the future
My mind in the now is combining all three
This moment becomes every moment.

You are ready for the Creative Leap!

Mihalyi Csikszentmihalyi also relates passion directly to the attribute of creativity. From 1990 to 1995, Csikszentmihalyi and his students at the University of Chicago videotaped interviews with a group of 91 "exceptional individuals," people who (a) had made a difference to a major domain of culture (sciences, arts, business, government, or human well-being in general), (b) were still actively involved, and (c) were over 60 years old. From these interviews, 10 dimensions of complexity were developed, the "real characteristics of creative persons." His ninth dimension states, "most creative persons are very passionate about their work, yet they can be extremely objective about it as well."[85] Yes.

The research identified an energy generated by this conflict between attachment and detachment, an energy that was mentioned by many of the respondents as being an important part of their work. Csikszentmihalyi believed that the reason for this was relatively clear. "Without the passion, we soon lose interest in a difficult task. Yet without being objective about it, our work is not very good and lacks credibility. So, the creative process tends to be what some respondents called a yin-yang alternation between these two extremes."[86] This movement from passion to objectivity, from action to reflection, was called out by respondents as what allowed them to keep learning and adjusting to new situations. "Their creativity unfolded organically from idea to action, then through the evaluation of the outcomes of action back to ideas—a cycle that repeated itself again and again."[87] This tension is also part of the experiential learning model.[88] As Alex penned her thoughts one morning on a scrape piece of paper:

My passion overcame me
And I acted before thinking,
Then, upon further reflection,
Understood my reaction.

Surprising new thought emerged
As contemplation continued
Leading to sighting new actions
With far better conclusions

Still the cycle continues
Even better ideas emerge
Bringing expanding and learning
And new ways of living life.

It seems we are never done.

Dorothy Leonard and Walter Swap noted the movement from Taylorism (where people were hired for their muscle) through total quality (where people were hired for their muscle and brains) to knowledge work (where people are hired for their muscle, brains and passion). "This passion is what gets people up in the morning . . . and it can come in the form of passion for the job, for innovation, or for the organization."[89] Built on intrinsic and extrinsic motivators, Leonard and Swap noted that it is passion that "fuels creativity," then presented dozens of examples that support their statements. For example, a former Harley-Davidson CEO, Richard Teerlink, explained:

We didn't want people who just come to work. We wanted people to be excited about what they do, to have an emotional attachment to our company. It was the excitement they got when they were standing in line in the supermarket wearing a Harley T-shirt and someone said, "Do you work at Harley? Wow!' We got people who wanted to work for this kind of company, who wanted to make a difference.[90]

Leonard and Swap believed that real enthusiasm is contagious. They quoted Fisher-Price's Lisa Mancuso: "I love the product; I feel passion for what I do … I couldn't champion something I didn't love."[91] And before leaving these authors, we cite one more finding, "Passion and enthusiasm thrive in an atmosphere of optimism and confidence in the future."[92]

Amabile and Polanyi have also, separately, presented significant evidence of the importance of passion alongside personal investment to spur creativity and engage the persistent effort required to develop expertise or create significant innovations in a domain.[93]

Passion and Leadership

In their work on leadership credibility, James Kouzes and Barry Posner discussed both exhibiting and encouraging passion as an important leadership attribute.

"When we talk about what we love to do, gain a deeper understanding of others, share more intimately, and truly enjoy the interaction, our energy and passion are contagious. By caring, loving, and showing compassion, we can release a spirit in people that is unequaled. This is something that we can do in business every day."[94]

Interestingly, Kouzes and Posner related leadership passion to suffering in their discussion of credibility. They believed that the most passionate people are those who have suffered the most, those who have "risked their independence, their fortunes, their health, and sometimes their lives for people and a purpose beyond themselves. Passion earned from suffering is inspiring. Leaders who are truly inspirational, who demonstrate courage and passion, are the first to suffer."[95]

> The most passionate people are those who have suffered the most. *Passion earned from suffering is inspiring. Leaders who are truly inspirational, who demonstrate courage and passion, are the first to suffer.*
>
> -James Kouzes and Barry Posner

Even before Alex officially became a teenager, she was torn by the events of the larger world and the feelings of pain perceived in her personal microcosm. She read the work of John Paul Sartre, absorbing the feelings of Existentialism, while simultaneously believing there had to be something better, something greater. In an early poem written during this period, it was perhaps the father who adopted and raised her who served as the model for the champion in this uphill battle with life. Alex's father—an immigrant from Greece with a 7th grade formal education and a heart of gold—was the wisest man she knew until she met her later life partner, David. In this poetic treatment, a leader pushes toward the light, overcoming both the existential burdens of life and those of his own making, risking all—and ultimately giving his life—for future generations.

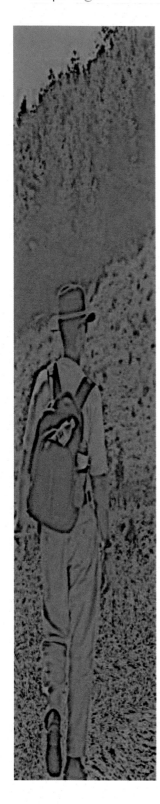

His wrinkled cheeks were streaked with sweat,
The product of his load.
His hair was white, his frame was bent,
Quite in the ancient mode.

His eyes were clear, the distance searched,
A glint of light he sought.
And deep within his soul he knew
The suffering he had brought.

He leaned upon a sturdy branch
He'd borrowed from an oak.
And shouldering his taxing load
He still enjoyed life's joke.

Within the sack his burden stirred
And uttered broken moans.
They turned his blood to burning wine
And petrified his bones.

He said his prayers as onward still
His feet were wont to go.
While in the sack his burden moaned
A challenge to its foe.

The light appeared and caught his eyes
And forward he was urged.
While on his back in writhing pain
His sins and deeds were purged.

Louder moaned the wriggling form
And louder still it screamed.
The bundle tossed and bulged and turned
And ripped where it was seamed.

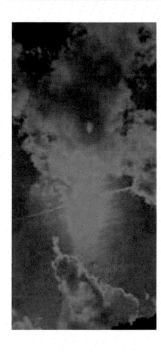

The old man's eyes were filled with tears
As blood rushed down his back.
But still he urged his body on
While holding tight the crack.

And with a final, rending push
He reached the brightest light.
His burden screamed and fell in death,
The old man's eyes shone bright.

He kneeled, and with his final breath
He whispered this to me:
"He cannot hurt you now, my child,
Be what you need to be."

The relationship between leadership and passion is not new to the literature. John Maxwell cited passion as one of the 21 indispensable qualities of a leader, becoming the person others will want to follow. He saw passion as the first step to achievement and stated that passion increases your willpower, changes you and makes the impossible possible. In summary, "Nothing can take the place of passion in a leader's life."[96]

Peters and Austin said that leadership connotes "unleashing energy, building, freeing, and growing."[97] They further stated, "We must cultivate passion and trust, and at virtually the same moment we must delve unmercifully into the details. How do we do it, or at least make a beginning? That's what *A Passion for Excellence* is all about."[98]

Joe Batten called his article based on go-givers instead of go-getters as, "Servant-leadership: A passion to serve."[99] Lad and Luechauer discuss five pathways to achieve servant-leadership (cognitive, experiential, spiritual, organizational and community). "Each of the approaches encourages passionate commitment, action, and a sense of urgency on behalf of the leader."[100]

In answering the question of whether leaders are born or made, Charles Handy responded that **if you find something you're passionate about, then you have got one of the three elements of being a true leader.**[101] Neff and Citrin interviewed 50 business leaders who have achieved what they term as extraordinary success. While these leaders demonstrated a wide range of personalities and styles and represented a cross section of the population, they identified 10 traits that these leaders appeared to have in common. No trait appeared more noticeable than that of passion for their people and companies. "Quite simply, they love what they do. In many ways, passion is the counterpart of ... Doing the Right Things Right, inspiring employees to achieve greatness."[102] For example, Dole states, "Having a passion for what you do, a sense of mission that comes from the heart, gives you the energy, drive and enthusiasm that's contagious and essential for leading an organization."[103]

Passionate leadership is a term used by Chip Bell, who believes that the reason some leaders are embraced while others are rejected has little to do with reason, but everything to do with passion. Bell asserted that *passion is more honest than reason*. Passion "makes us feel free, alive, and somehow 'a real, whole person' and, when leaders surface that feeling in us, we are somehow more energized, more like a knight ready for battle."[104]

Philosopher/psychologist Rollo May believes **there is an energy field between humans**, and that when a person reaches out in passion, others answer with passion. Bell sums this up, "Passionate connections provoke passionate responses. Leadership is fundamentally about influencing."[105] Anita Roddick, The Body Shop founder, agreed, "We communicate with passion—and passion persuades."[106] Bell went on to say:

> People may be instructed by reason, but they are inspired by passion ... Why are you here, in this role, at this time? What difference will you being here make? What legacy will you leave behind? Will you be forgotten for what you maintained or remembered for what you added? Imposing mountains are climbed, culture-changing movements are started, and breakthrough miracles are sparked by leaders who took the governors off rationalism and prudence, letting their spirit ascent from within.[107]

Sara Melendez says, "Effective leaders are passionate about the cause they are promoting and about their commitment to the greater or public good."[108] We pointed this out earlier. And, again, in affirmation, recall that Peter Senge says that people's passions flow naturally into creating something that truly excites them. "The passion at the heart of every great undertaking comes from **the deep longing of human beings to make a difference**, to have an impact. It comes from what you contribute rather than from what you get."[109] [emphasis added]

VI: Thought Leader Passion

In 2005, Alex published a research study exploring aspects of Knowledge Management that contributed to the passion expressed by its thought leaders. The study engaged 34 thought leaders across four continents. Thought leaders link their passion to a higher order, and consider passion itself a reward. Thought leader values were closely connected with the field, and, in the words of one thought leader, "Somehow I've matched up people's value systems with a process." One interpretation of these intense connections is the resonance of the field with our fundamental nature as human beings, those things identified in the framework that contain the seeds of passion itself.

The field of KM itself, and what it represents in terms of external events and stimuli such as knowledge sharing, networks, and so forth, is in the words of thought leaders a tool for *living in the world and with the world in a more human and humane way*.

Thought leaders see the field of Knowledge Management as a tool for living in the world and with the world in a more human and humane way.

One way of thinking about this is by considering a focus area such as knowledge sharing. Certainly, in an organizational setting, sharing knowledge associated with the work at hand through community and team structures has a direct impact on organizational efficiency and effectiveness in terms of such things as solving problems, creating new and better ways to work, and preventing repetition of previous mistakes. However, this knowledge sharing also builds relationships and facilitates learning and understanding, *which connotes larger engagement of the individual in the world in which they live*, going beyond the work environment. This translates into a larger impact of the individual in and on society and, in an autopoetic system, feedback to the individual, thereby promoting growth.

The following graphic is a collage of thought leader responses when describing what excited them about the field of KM.

"KM is Significant Because It Fits Right Upon This Historical Opportunity."

THE WORLD IS CHANGING ...

- Collective world change
- World as living network
- Moving into new global governance ... dynamic relationship
- Knowledge will be global discriminator

Be the change you want to be ...
-Mahatma Ghandi

- Paradoxical moment ... Power darkening planet ... forces at war around us ... Moment in evolution of potential extreme importance.

- Most dangerous times in our history ... The best of times and worst of times at the same time.

- We as a human species are reinventing ourselves.

Characteristics of KM from a world view:
Honors humanity; Has a human and humane agenda; Reaffirms faith in people; Enriches awareness of livingness; Honors value of human judgment; Uses tools of meaning from belonging to human society; Multiplies brain power; is reducing ignorance; Helps us recognize we are a part of the world in a very deep way.

To help transform the world we need to:
Honor the world; Generate a further level of consciousness; Get across this idea of understanding other people's perspectives; Find better ways of embracing the Knowledge movement and beyond.

Knowledge and Knowledge Management are "predecessors to higher-level understanding and meaning" ... They offer:

- The promise of a difference in human experience
- An opportunity for evolution into a qualitatively different reality.
- Nourishment and cultivation of the future.
- The potential to create a platform for world peace.

Knowledge Management is ... Bringing questions onto the planet. Certain questions have the power to change the world ... Providing a systems perspective for *raising the level of consciousness* for man. Part of the new consciousness. A new way of looking at the world ... *Ushering in advances for humanity.* Helping us move as a world towards responsibility and peace ... A quest to have more wisdom about the world ... *A vehicle for co-evolution as a species.* Providing the possibility to overcome the fundamental contradiction between biological constitution and civilization.

Embedded in KM is some kind of spiritual wonder of what this world is about.

It is not surprising that thought leaders themselves have passion. As introduced earlier in this chapter, it has been confirmed through well-grounded studies that reason and passion are both critical to our ability to make proper decisions, and passion has been linked with intellectual pursuits, leadership, and creativity, all clearly part of thought leadership.

Passion was also identified in the thought leader response as **an attribute of being a thought leader**. For example, when describing thought leaders, one responder noted, "They all have a passion of one sort or another. I think that fuels continuous thought and desire for clarity . . . that's the way it is for me." Another responder affirmed, "You can tell it in any of them . . . in the tone of their voice, and their excitement, and you know it's contagious."

This thought leader passion was described in many ways. For example, "If you believe it you try to show it to others" and "I guess they all have a sense of mission, and this is sometimes even close to religion or emotional feeling that you have a mission to achieve and that you need to open the eyes of the people." This latter responder goes on to explain, "This is also the reason why so many people in this field are so involved in educational projects or supporting this at the societal level." These insights are not isolated in the response and clearly agree with the research cited in this book. So, it is forwarded that *passion is a natural aspect of thought leadership*.

The thought leader passion that came from specific aspects of the knowledge management field was considered an additional reward by many thought leaders. Thus, the passion felt by these thought leaders is very positive, and helped fuel their personal energy, their personal satisfaction, and the love for their work.

Although some of these leaders admit they were passionate people, a number of responses gave support to the claim that as part of that passion there were values and aspirations of a higher order of meaning. For example, in thought leader words:

"nourishment and cultivation of the future"
"the richness of multidimensionality of experience"
"value of knowledge and what it can do for society, for individuals,
   for interactions between individuals"
"the creation of new ideas"
"overall human value"
"I'm not wasting my time"
"I'm making a contribution" and
"work really worthy."

Such responses as these—and many others—indicate that thought leader passion was not just for their work but also for **the higher good to which their work contributes**. This overall response would indicate that *thought leader passion is derived from a higher order*.

An interesting finding from this study[110] is patterns of passion levels described by thought leaders ranging from the time they entered the field of Knowledge Management to the time they were interviewed. Of the 34 thought leaders, at one end of the spectrum 4 (12%) were early developers of the field, 17 (50%) had been in the field 8-10 years, and, at the other end of the spectrum, 3 (9%) had been less than eight years in the field. There was great diversity in their experiences as academic practitioners, consulting practitioners and organizational practitioners. As one participant so well described, "Each person's journey into knowledge management is a story. It's a narrative … it's got its own cast of characters, models, problems, tribulations, all that stuff." Indeed, that is a good description of each person's journey in life!

Thirteen of the TLs visualized their passion levels. Here's what those looked like:

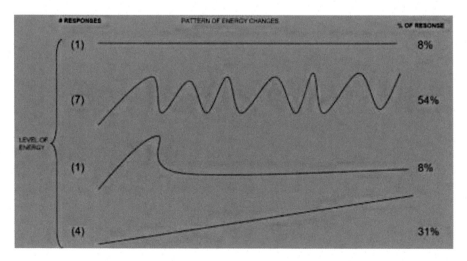

The individual who felt that her energy had stayed the same (top pattern) said she was always incredibly curious and that, while sometimes this got in her way, KM was absolutely always a passion for her. The four who felt their energy had increased (bottom pattern) offered varied explanations. For example, one said that his energy had moved from potential to kinetic to "almost frenetic energy."

Another said that he had more energy now because he's a much wiser guy than he was 20 years previously. Another said that it started being a "gut" feel, and now she could see "much more consistent signs that this is the right track."

The up and down movement cited by the largest number of responders (second from top) is similar to the pattern described by Csikszentmihalyi linking passion and creativity, whose research identified an energy generated by the conflict between attachment and detachment, what Csikszentmihalyi called a yin-yang alternation between passion and objectivity. Specifically—an idea that was introduced and discussed in the previous chapter—Csikszentmihalyi said, "Their creativity unfolded organically from idea to action, then through the evaluation of the outcomes of action back to ideas—a cycle that repeated itself again and again."[111]

With that thought in mind, we discover a model that looks something like this:

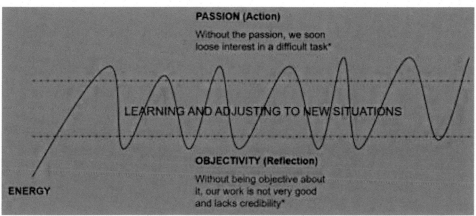

As one thought leader in this group says of their passion, "It rises and falls like circadian rhythms and all that." *Circadian rhythms* is the term given to the daily rhythmic activity cycle (24 hour interval) of many biological organisms, similar to the rise and fall of tides. Another thought leader actually described this process in words similar to our model:

Well, there was a period of high passion when I was actually implementing theory in action, you could say ... Then my interest waned, then caught a renewed push when the interest in KM made people also show an interest in my early work, and I got more enthusiastic toward the end of the 90's when I could see a shift in the trend away from IT and technology and more towards people.

Another responder likened her energy fluctuations waxing and waning with the redefining of the field. And another explained, "Like everyone, we have highs and lows that are tied to specific happenings in the environment. It's not dissimilar to the way electrical circuits work, where you have a transient period of highs and lows, and the you reach the steady state."

And in this thought we have reached a level of wisdom. Knowledge is at the very core of who we are as human beings. By definition, it is how we effectively take information and successfully apply it to real-world situations. Thus, thought leaders focusing on knowledge as the foundation of a field of learning, connecting and sharing would indeed follow the highs and lows of people.

A Potential Conversation

Combining her passion for writing—and in recognition of the power of intellectual passion—Alex created a story to help convey the passion felt by thought leaders in the field of Knowledge Management. Her characters are having a conversation in the library of the Mountain Quest Institute.

Sy, a cognitive psychologist recognized for his ground-breaking work on judgment and decision-making as well as creative approaches to internal motivation, sits on one of the burgundy leather couches of the Mountain Quest Institute, reflecting on the research results he has just read. Across from him is Ivan, an international businessman whose specialty is knowledge-based organizations addressing the multicultural challenges of global business. Next to Ivan sits Bianca, a biologist interested in the application of living systems to organizations, and angled into an adjacent chair is Fern, a futurist specializing in global trends at the intersection of technology, culture, economics and management.

Sy looks up at the others and speaks, "I am somewhat surprised—actually, amazed is a better word—that this field, admittedly which I know little about, can contain within itself so many of the key elements that excite us as human beings. We all value knowledge—that's core to being human—but the field seems to couple that knowledge core with the characteristics of sharing and creating and acting on knowledge that not only offer the possibility of improving our organizations, but make each of us as individuals feel good about our own personal growth and contribution. As Csikszentmihalyi explains, in the West we have historically thought of ourselves as individuals whereas Asian and African cultures see themselves as nodes in a network of relationships.[112] In reading this research I got the sense that many of the thought leaders interviewed saw themselves as nodes in a large—perhaps global—network. Perhaps knowledge workers in knowledge organizations also see themselves that way."

Ivan nods, "That's an interesting perspective, Sy, howbeit speculative. But as a global businessman my primary concern has to be how to create businesses that live long, maintain competitive advantage and stay profitable. Relative to those goals, I'm not sure how well knowledge management will be able to contribute, although, of course, intuitively I understand the importance of managing knowledge assets. Now, something I've learned about this field from both my experience and what I've read is its power to move organizations away from the bureaucratic, control-oriented mindset toward recognizing and giving individuals more freedom, influence, and opportunity to contribute to the organization's mission and direction. What do you think Bianca?"

"Well, what you say certainly makes sense," Bianca responds. "But I'd like to propose that looking at knowledge-centric organizations—those organizations that have learned how to empower their knowledge workers, increase innovation and at the same time maintain cohesion—they have done very well. Birkinshaw has recently addressed this challenge in an MIT *Sloan Management Review* article interview about his new book.[113] We should all be aware that there's a lot of recent work that's being done in the area of complexity theory that relates to the researcher's remarks that a KM organization, or more appropriately perhaps the field of KM itself, could be considered a complex adaptive system. For example, to meet the rapidly changing demands of the marketplace requires both our organizations and the KM field to continuously learn and adapt or get left behind."

Fern breaks in. "Bianca, I think you're on track. In my work looking at global futures I see a definite trend moving us away from standard industrial age management and thinking toward a much more challenging and uncertain future. I'd like to suggest that the acronym CUCA describes this future, in the sense that our world is one of accelerating *change*, rising *uncertainty*, rapidly growing *complexity*, and increasing *anxiety* in response to that change, uncertainty and complexity.[114] As the research points out, information is growing exponentially and knowledge builds on knowledge. These phenomena do not seem to be leveling off and, frankly, I'm seriously concerned about our ability as a species to handle this. Bianca, could you elaborate a bit on just exactly what is a complex adaptive system? This may be helpful in finding a way to deal with this challenging CUCA environment."

"Sure, Fern, I'd be happy to. The concept originated years ago in biology in a new, closely associated field of study called general systems theory. A complex system is one which has so many interrelated parts that it is impossible to trace causal effects, or detail influences or relationships. As Battram has proposed, a complex adaptive system is not only complex but also self-organizing, continuously learning and, of course, changing its internal structure to adapt."[115]

Ivan interjects, "Go back for a minute—are you saying we can't use logic and detailed information to make rational decisions?"

Sy jumps in, "Let me answer, Ivan. Unfortunately, I think you're for the most part right, although what we think of as rational decisions certainly still has a role in decision-making. Let's take the field of knowledge management for example. The direction of the field as it evolves is the result of a large number of knowledge workers and thought leaders making rational decisions, acting on hunches, creating new ideas and pursuing possibilities. This is so because no one is capable of foreseeing or even understanding the future and—as chaos theory has taught us—small changes can sometimes lead to extraordinary results.[116] In other words, the direction of the KM field emerges from the actions, decisions, creativity and intuitive thinking of many different individuals. But realize that we're all in the same boat as our organizations become more knowledge-centric and more complex. All of us have grown up from an industrial history which has naturally led us to learn to make decisions—and act on those decisions—from the premise that we live in a deterministic world where the more information we have and the more rational our thought the better our decisions.[117] And while certainly this is true for many areas of our work—those areas that still function in simple cause-and-effect environments—as Fern points out, as our milieu becomes more complex we have to recognize that it is not possible to use only logic and analysis."

"That's a good point," Bianca says, "Because not only is complexity very challenging to understand, it is essentially unpredictable to various degrees.[118] There's what is called an emergent phenomenon in complex organizations. Examples are culture, consciousness, and knowledge itself that arise from multiple interactions within a complex system and take on characteristics entirely different than the components of the system. The field of knowledge management is undoubtedly a complex system because there are far too many people, too many relationships, too many ideas, and too many organizations involved to ever truly "understand" the relationships among them and the details of what happens. Yet, books are written, trends appear, patterns become clear, and the overall field does have a 'cone of direction' even though its path may appear random and is unpredictable."

Ivan leans forward on his seat. "Bianca, are you saying that the KM field has no leader, no strategy or direction? If that is the case then is it simply a random group of well-meaning people? This doesn't make sense to me."

Bianca responds, "This self-organization occurs in many complex adaptive systems! It just bubbles up from the large number of interactions, relationships and goals of the many workers—or we could add the term thought leaders—in the field. Also, recall that knowledge itself, when coupled with learning and sharing, forms a common bond that helps the overall field take on slowly changing patterns. For example, the research mentioned several emergent phenomena such as storytelling, communities of practice, living networks and the current movement toward personal knowledge management."

"Bianca, does this mean that as a businessman I will no longer have control over my organization? Not that I always feel like I'm in control, but if I don't have control how can I be responsible for it? Senior executives and government leaders are expected to be in control of their organizations and accountable for them, and now you're telling me because the future is becoming more complex, more of this CUCA stuff, that knowledge and KM are describing a situation in which there's no such thing as real control?"

Sy looks at Ivan smiling. "Well, it sounds like you intuitively recognize, of course, that we as individuals are rarely in control anyway. What's happening now, as we move toward a knowledge society, is that organizations are moving from the highly-controlled organizations of the early 1900s that spurred Taylorism in the auto production lines and generations of simulated sweat shops, toward an environment which will no longer be dominated by organizations. In other words, in this new paradigm if organizations mimic the field of KM and become more like complex adaptive systems, they must scan, observe, interpret and adapt to the environment in addition to, of course, influencing where and what they can."

Bianca jumps in excitedly. "That is absolutely right, and this field of knowledge management offers a good example. The field must adapt to the needs of its customers, which are organizations and corporations, in the sense that if it doesn't produce value added it will have to struggle to survive, no matter how self-worthy it is."

"And what we have seen," Fern offers, "is a significant movement within the field from its initial focus on technology and information towards knowledge in terms of understanding and the social aspects of knowledge creation as the predominate value contributors. This is an example of its learning and adaptability."

Sy agrees. "Yes, and that's exactly why the field of knowledge management is moving us towards recognizing the significance and importance of humans and individuals and learning and sharing to create value added. It is internally and naturally evolving in the human direction: giving the individual the freedom and responsibility needed for success within the vision and direction of their organization."

Bianca softly exclaims, "Ah, ha! You have just identified a significantly new emergent property of the field of knowledge management."

"A question," Ivan interjects. "Does this mean that the field will survive if it continues to offer value to its customers while adapting to the needs of a changing world?"

Bianca nods, "From a biological point of view, every complex adaptive system must have energy and information coming in, and it must be able to continuously create new ideas and change its infrastructure to adapt to the demands of its environment. **In the case of the KM field, its energy comes from the passion of its thought leaders—and most likely knowledge workers as well—and the human desire to learn and understand.**"

Sy jumps in, "And I think part of that passion is the opportunity to create new ideas, processes and applications, and to better understand the process of developing and exploring our own cognitive limits through personal study, team collaboration and other methods of leverage. Also, I would suggest that the field of knowledge management has an inherent internal growth mechanism which would aid its survival. Since knowledge builds on both exponentially growing information and on knowledge itself, by its nature the field of knowledge management builds upon itself. I guess that's what is meant by the researcher saying the field is self-referential."

"That's certainly true," Fern offers, "although the researcher was pointing out that what thought leaders were doing themselves as thought leaders and practitioners is exactly what they are helping others to learn how to do. But I think this is also because we know the explosion of technology has reduced the cost of communication, emphasized the creation of networks, sped up transactions, and allowed knowledge workers to confront the challenge of understanding and dealing with complexity.

"Yes, but recognize," Sy suggests, "that we're only at the beginning of this transition into the age of complexity, and frankly no one really understands how or what we as a species need to do."

Bianca offers, "However, this field of KM has helped awakened many of us to the importance of continuous learning, knowledge sharing, and understanding what's happening. This may be the beginning of a changing world."

"Well, from my psychologist perspective," Sy says, "I certainly understand why autotelic work is so frequently found within the field of KM and why the field seems to have a magnetic attraction to many people. It both supports our own personal deep desire for understanding and growing as well as being able to contribute to the broader good of organizations and families, and even the greater good."

"If it can do all that," Ivan says excitedly, "and in addition create a new value proposition which improves our economy, our affluence level, and helps developing countries have a better standard of living, then this field should be recognized for its potential."

Sy laughs. "Well, I don't disagree, except to add that it's really people who will do all that, howbeit people who are both more knowledgeable and connected through living networks, and people who are supported by everything this field pushes us to focus on. So, our focus is not so much on people as assets, but people as investors, investing time, energy and intelligence."[119]

Fern, who has been listening carefully, reflects on the dialogue before saying, "Ivan, I don't know whether you're aware of it, but some developing countries are already using the field to leapfrog developed countries through bypassing industrial development and moving directly into the knowledge world. First of all, besides needing natural land resources, industrialization takes a great deal of capital and time, and developing countries don't have much of either. But because many people around the world have access to satellites, Internet, cell phones, and so forth, they are aware of what other countries have. This creates intense pressures within developing countries to improve their standard of living."

"Now that you point that out, Fern," Bianca responds, "perhaps the field of KM as a complex adaptive system is spreading its wings far enough to potentially become a world-wide phenomenon."

"That's an interesting possibility," Sy says. "I do know that if we had world-wide communication and recognition of the importance of learning, sharing and innovation that the knowledge management field promotes, then technology coupled with living networks could help the world become closer and more collaborative rather than so competitive and divisive. In our multinational enterprises we've already recognized that our exposure to a wider variety of customers, competitors and technologies stimulate innovation by helping us sense and respond to a diverse array of environmental signals. Then, we have the ability to tap into the resources and capabilities of a rich knowledge-creating network. That means better responses to choose from, and the ability to proliferate certain innovations.[120] Living networks may well move us toward a win-win world."

"Living networks would certainly change the global business arena," Ivan notes.

"What a fascinating possibility," Fern suggests, "that something as seemingly benign as the field of knowledge management could become significant as a world movement."

"Well, I can tell you this," Bianca responds, "historically very few living organisms have been able to survive the test of evolution unless they *were* complex adaptive organisms. As we all know, Darwin learned that many years ago."[121]

"But aren't we, as individuals, *intelligent* complex adaptive organizations?" Sy poses with a smile. "So that hopefully when we start working together that intelligence connected by need and a willingness to learn and share can do better than any other living organisms."

Fern sighs, "Did you notice that the researcher applies the word intelligent to the field? Let me confirm that language." She flips through the pages in front of her. "Yes, the researcher does say that the field of knowledge management is an intelligent complex adaptive system."

Sy responds, "I'm not really sure how a field could be intelligent—other than the sum of the individual actions and contributions by its thought leaders and workers are connected sufficiently through communications and the sharing of understanding such that there can emerge a mode of behavior and an intention of force which moves the field in a direction for its survival and contribution."

Thinking carefully, Bianca responds, "That's a fascinating idea, Sy. There is a concept called 'swarm intelligence' that comes from the amazing ability of ants and some other insects to change their individual behavior when needed so that the swarm, as a whole, adapts to, and takes advantage of changes in its environment. 'Perhaps the most powerful insight from swarm intelligence is that complex collective behavior can emerge from individuals following simple rules."[122]

"You know the more I reflect on this field," Ivan mutters, "the more important I think it may become in all of our futures."

Fern responds quickly, "I know from my work viewpoint I'm going to follow this with intense interest, and do some serious study to understand it better."

"That's a task that it would behoove all of us to take on with passion," Sy states emphatically.

"Yes, I agree," Bianca says excitedly, "because I think each of us with our own special expertise—and many other people looking at the field from their own experiential viewpoint and areas of interest and work—will help improve our collective understanding of what's going on, what we need to do, and the possibilities for the future."

"Isn't that the concept of a living network?" Ivan asks.

An interesting observation emerging from this research study is that EVERYONE has the potential of being a thought leader in some domain of knowledge when they—through their passion—place continuous focused attention on that domain. In other words, what we focus our energy on and learn about day after day is the area where we develop the ability to recognize patterns and relationships, which can lead to new ways of thinking. Take a few minutes to reflect on something that has held your interest over the years, an area of passion. What do you know about this area? Do others recognize your knowledge in this area?

Remember, we are experiential learners, which means that we learn best through experiences. And while that may or may not include formal education, it DOES include travel, relationships, business dealings, and the unique skill sets each of us acquires as we move through the school of life. There's something that YOU are driven to discover, pushed to accomplish.

As Cindy describes that churning need inside which propels her to capture her thoughts and feelings, she shares: Driven, pulling force is strong, burning, yearning inside, something's going on. Looking to uncover, out of sight taking flight, driven to discover. Center, focusing, with intent, circumvent, search for opening. Thought all consuming, strategize, scrutinize, discovery blooming. And poetically, she writes:

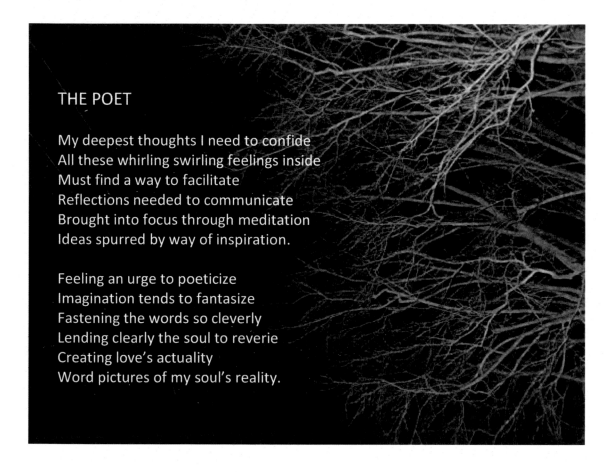

THE POET

My deepest thoughts I need to confide
All these whirling swirling feelings inside
Must find a way to facilitate
Reflections needed to communicate
Brought into focus through meditation
Ideas spurred by way of inspiration.

Feeling an urge to poeticize
Imagination tends to fantasize
Fastening the words so cleverly
Lending clearly the soul to reverie
Creating love's actuality
Word pictures of my soul's reality.

VII: The Passions of the Spirit

Passion has long been associated with religious contexts. As introduced in Chapter I, in the Biblical context the Passion (capital "P") refers to the ultimate suffering of Jesus Christ on the cross. The Passion story is about how God, in the human form of Jesus, suffered the same life experiences of fear, pain, doubt, injustice and, ultimately, death as the ordinary person experiences. Note the relation of the word passion to "suffering", as emerged in our conversation of leadership and passion.

The concept of passion also plays a significant role in the Five Buddha Families of Vajrayana Buddhism. This teaching describes processes for the transmutation of the five major energies (anger, pride, passion, jealousy and apathy) and the emotions connected to these energies.

The Vajrayana approach looks at these energies as part of the spiritual path—the stronger an emotion, the more useful it can be as a vehicle for awakening. Awakening is the aim of consciousness, the Buddha's state of mind, the only state in which even pain and suffering are borne with ease.[123]

Alan Watts described awakening in this manner, "If you were awake, you would understand that you and the whole universe are pretending: projecting yourself at the point called here and now in the form of a human organism."[124] The Dali Lama, certainly a definitive source on Buddhism, defined the verbal root of Buddhism as, "to waken from the sleep of ignorance and spread one's intelligence to everything that can be known."[125] Passion, then, is viewed as a strong vehicle for awakening.

> If you were awake, you would understand that you and the whole universe are pretending: projecting yourself at the point called here and now in the form of a human organism.
>
> -Alan Watts

Each of the five major energies has both negative and positive potential for the individual, and it is part of the individual's growth process to work through the negative and transform these energies into positive forces in their lives. Of the negative aspect of passion, Tara Bennett-Goleman stated that,

> Passion, in the sense of neurotic clinging, grasping, and craving, can manifest itself as a hysteric's shallow seductiveness, or as the hypnotic charisma of a manipulative con artist. It manifests as an alluring, pleasing and always seductive pursuit of objects of desire.[126]

This energy, when transmuted, takes the form of discriminating awareness, "taking a precise interest in, and paying keen attention to, whatever presents itself. This ever-inquisitive awareness opens up communication: other people are seen and understood in their full distinctiveness, and related to with empathy and a warm compassion."[127]

We create our reality based on passion, which is energy that helps people speak from the heart and engage others.

Irina Rockwell went so far as to state that **we create our reality based on passion**. Passion is referred to as "Padma energy," energy that helps people speak from the heart and "draw out other people and engage them ... This sense of pleasure and promise magnetizes others."[128]

On the negative side, Rockwell said that people have to "engage their passion without losing sight of the danger of getting caught up in or intoxicated by it . . . we don't want to eliminate their passion; we want to cultivate it, refine it."[129]

Similarly, to the religions of India who draw their fundamental teachings from the Bhagavad Gita and Upanishads,

> The most basic human struggle is not the external quest for food, shelter, or a mate . . . but rather the attempt to rule our passions—our internal desires and cravings. If they are not contained by meditative practice, or restrained by practical reason, or expressed by wholesome habits, or transcended by conscious awakening, the incessant grasping gives rise to attachments, which are thought to be the source of all our suffering.[130]

According to Lou Marinoff, the Jewish Cabalists, the Christian Gnostics, the Islamic Sufis, the Hindu Brahmanas and the Buddhist awakened ones all teach theories, techniques, and methods for reasonably guiding the self's passions.[131] Sooner or later they all lead to the center of oneself, the concept described as awakening.

Recognizing that religions are man-made constructs in service of worshipping a higher energy, both Cindy and Alex have moved in and out of various religions—and perceived religions—over the course of their lives, while always sustaining strong spiritual connections to that something larger. Cindy, whose mother left her for years at a time, lived through physical and emotional abuse you hope will never happen to a child.

For Alex, the early daily abuse was mental and emotional and largely conveyed by the older sister, who held the memory of being ripped away from her mother and, since all this happened after the new baby was born, blamed the younger sister for this event. Yet, even as youngsters in the midst of perceived and legitimate hardships and physical and emotional pain, at their lowest moments of despair, the urge to call out for help from a higher source would bubble up. As a young Alex wrote during a moment of despair:

> Divine injustice that grips this wretched soul of mine
> Release!
> Fling away the deep depression that captivates my mind
> Release!
>
> O God who has guided me through the very depths of sin
> Forgive!
> How long can I stand the tears, the sobs, the sweat of men
> Forgive!

Within much of the early writing of both Cindy and Alex, there seems to be an overlap of both victimhood and a feeling of guilt. Looking back—and after our discussion in the previous chapter—perhaps this has very much to do with the ups and downs, highs and lows, of the human condition? When we perceive ourselves as victims, as things happening that are out of our control, then we *are* victims. When things happen that perhaps we COULD have affected in some way, and when we have the perception that some related (or unrelated) action we took was wrong—that is, not consistent with our values and beliefs—then we tend to carry some level of guilt, which may or may not be actually connected with the topic or event at hand. And, knowingly or unknowingly, consciously or unconsciously, we search for ways to move through these feelings and come into alignment with our inner selves.

For example, even as a child in the midst of heart-breaking events, Cindy reached out through her poetry, seeking that strength within the core of her that was emerging. Alex cries when she reads this verse.

BIRTHDAY UNDER A BUSH

Still here, not understanding why
So very sad, can't even cry
No longer know where I belong
Everything in life feels wrong.

Squeezed in tight like a human wedge
Memories tucked in under the hedge
From myself I'm trying to hide
In this lonely backyard, outside.

Birthday fourteen, for goodness sake
Even made my own birthday cake
Yard's so quiet and no one's about
No songs, no candles to blow out.

Can this bush and I become one?
In this hedge, gazing at the sun
Oh, living leaves somewhat shading
All too soon just a memory fading.

Frozen birthday moment in time
Soon this home no longer is mine
Never to belong here evermore
Pushing through that revolving door!

Later in life, Cindy penned moments that had been too painful to write as a child, the events that laid the foundation of the shame, guilt and fear she carried through childhood. The writing served as a release, while those early experiences—and the ones that followed as she fought her way out of victimhood—forged her depth of thought and feeling, a passion which she chose to direct and guide her expanding beliefs, her personal growth, and her motherhood of five children.

INNOCENCE LOST

Innocence lost, taken long before time
Leaves the little lamb anything but fine
Who can this child turn to for affection?
Virtue robbed through a perceived infection.

Lost beseeched soul who is doomed not to bloom
Life's transformation came along too soon
Naively looking at life through child eyes
Damaged inside, no one hears the still cries.

It takes many years to silence the pain
Through alcohol, drugs and acting insane
She'll travel countless roads till she can see
The guilt was not hers, and that sets her free!

It is not surprising that the concept of "awakening" became a focus of both Cindy's and Alex's lives, and as such threads its way through their writing. And again, and again, we see the idea of "release" and "freedom" emerge in Cindy's poetry. These were words that represented escape from the lives they felt had captured them, lives they ached to escape without a knowing of exactly how to go about that. Alex escaped through marriage, which brought both positive and negative events into her life. At 16, Cindy became a flower child, touching freedom and despair. As she believed, *without pain, we would not exist, so it needs to be embraced at all levels.* It was the 60's and 70's and she was a free spirit rebelling against structure and hunting for purpose. She died twice. And all of this accelerated her learning. And as the years passed, she did learn.

Awakening

Opening eyes are beginning to see
What was always right in front of me
Took a long time, this learning how
Had to look past the here and now.

Awareness explodes in my brain
All the demons are now restrained
If not for God, this would not be
I've been released, and I am free!

Perceiving a glow about the face
Reaching outward with imparted grace
Teaching with chosen conscious action
Exuding loving warm compassion

Listening with a heart of silence
Receiving and open to guidance
Feeling the pulse of humanity
Giving forward, acting selflessly

Hungering for agápē perfection
Opening in the Love Soul Connection

Then, there are defining events that occur in the course of life, moments of grace, sometimes expected and planned, and other times occurring in the instant, but forever changing the who you perceive you are. One such event happened to Alex while she was working for U.S. Fleet Activities, Yokosuka, Japan. Mother Teresa was invited to visit Camp Zama, which marked the first time she came onto a military base to speak. Alex, who was the then-editor of the base weekly newspaper, *The Seahawk*, was invited to interview Mother Teresa and photograph the event.

The article Alex wrote appeared in U.S. Navy newspapers around the world. More recently, she would relive this life-changing event through sharing it in a Conscious Look Book: *Possibilities that are YOU! Volume 4: Conscious Compassion*. Here is her story.

It's strange having a question repeatedly overtake the monkey chatter in our mind about an event that occurred 34 years ago! Well, that's exactly what's happening.

Thirty-four years ago, I was living in Yokosuka, Japan, on the U.S. Naval Base. This was an amazing time of life … I'd always wanted to live abroad, and the Japanese lifestyle and ceremony of life provided not only a rich taste of that dream, but oh so many learning experiences!

The day after arriving on Base, I was out hunting for a job, and within the week was hired as a part-time writer for the *Seahawk*, the Base weekly newspaper. There were over 40,000 military personnel and families living on and off the Base, and with the ships often out to sea, you can imagine the need to have support systems for those waiting for the Fleet to return.

There were lots of opportunities to make a difference. Since I'd had an early career in music, one of those ways was leading the various choirs through the all-Faith Chapel of Hope. Another was participating in some way in musicals. Another was manning the help hotline on Friday and Saturday nights. And another was through writing about the many discoveries available to all of us on and off Base. So, I did.

Pretty soon, that job was full-time, then, it was as the editor of the paper, expanding to include working with *Pacific Stars and Stripes* every week and writing columns for the English paper, *Tokyo Weekender*. I never knew what adventure was next!

Then, near the middle of November in 1984, I received a phone call that caused this little book to be such an important part of my life. For the first time in *her* life—and maybe the only time—Mother Teresa agreed to visit a military base.[19] She had spoken earlier at the International School in Tokyo, then visited a hospital in Hamamatsu. And from there, a U.S. Army C-12 flew her to Atsugi from where she was heloed to Camp Zama.

Mother was greeted by the Senior Chaplain of Camp Zama Chapel and a group of people who had worked with her mission in Tokyo. The Chaplain voiced all of our thoughts: "I can't say it's a once-in-a-lifetime experience because most people don't have it happen in their lifetime. It was one of those things that happens and I'm just happy to be a part of it." Together, the group joined in a meal of chicken, baked beans, bread and Indian tea with sugar and cream.

Then it was my turn. With Father Andre Gogaert sitting next to her on a sofa and me a couple of feet away on a facing chair, we spoke. She leaned towards me, perhaps a product of the bent form, and tilted her leathery face upward so that her eyes could take in my face, could follow my expression. Her mouth was slightly, knowingly, curled upward at the edges, laughing at the moment, and her eyes … and her eyes … I don't have the words.

She began in English, greeting me, asking after me, two old friends in a sweet embrace of caring. And then she would listen carefully as I asked questions, looking aside to Father Andre when she needed clarification, which was provided in French! And, that's the question that keeps popping up in my head: Why French?

Mother was born in 1910 in what is now Yugoslavia, and by the age of 18 had joined a group of Irish nuns in the Archdiocese of Calcutta, and then called to serve, to bring aid and dignity to the destitute in her adopted country of India. So why French? But perhaps that question interrupts the flow of the story.

On the other hand, did the story really begin in 1984? I think not. While I remember hearing about then-Sister Teresa on and off in my early years, this story began ten years earlier following a musical performance on a New York stage. Two little, old women (who were about my age now … but, alas, then I thought they were old!) came running backstage to get an autograph. Quite eloquently, I smiled and answered, "Of course!"

Taking hold of the program and a pen offered my way, my hand paused above the program. I couldn't remember my name! *Who was I?* Gosh, I'd played so many roles in my life, both on and off-stage. From the life stories people have shared with us when visiting the Mountain Quest Inn here in the Allegheny Mountains of West Virginia, I'm pretty sure *most* of us are living shifting lives full of lots of varied learning experiences!

Back home, reflecting on this event throughout the evening, I decided if I didn't know who I was, then I could CHOOSE who I am and who I wanted to be. So, I called to mind those people who I deeply admired and appreciated—my father, my mentor and Sister Teresa—and asked myself, **Why** *do I feel this way about them? While I can't be them, what traits do they exhibit that I can learn from and make my own?*

And there is the crux of this story. From Sister Teresa, I desired to learn persistence and *compassion.* Now, ten years later, in her presence, I could *feel* her compassion as she answered my questions, sometimes in English, and sometimes in French, which was translated by Father Andre.

"At the age of twelve I first knew I had a vocation to help the poor" she shared. This was consistent with what I had read about her. It was in her eighteenth year that she left to join the Sisters of Loretto. She took her first vows as a nun in 1928, and her final vows nine years later.

During her work of teaching and serving as principal at St. Mary's High School in Calcutta, her heart was greatly touched by the suffering children, lepers, and destitute ill outside the cloister walls. In 1946—the year before I was born—she received what she called a *call within a call.* "The message was clear." Her eyes sparkled as she said these words, and it was clear to me where that message came from! There was a small cross, anchored to her head wrap with a safety pen at the side of her head, that slightly fluttered as she moved her head to motion the Father to translate. She continued, "I was to leave the convent and help the poor, while living among them." This call came in 1948 at which time Mother Teresa founded the Society of the Missionaries of Charity in Calcutta's slums.

Now, these kinds of words have been written about her, maybe even the same words, since no doubt she had memorized them in English, but as she said them to me, they came from the wholeness of who she was. Now, *I* was leaning towards *her* and, occasionally in a gesture, an accent to a shared thought, we touched. Did we sit there talking an hour or two? I do not know how long it was.

When she went into the Camp Zama gymnasium to speak, twelve hundred expectant faces awaited her appearance. She did not disappoint. The 73-year-old, slight form entered the side door, paused to exchange smiles with a young child, and, with back bowed and hands clasped in front of her, edged gracefully up the stairs onto the platform, aided by Father Andre. I followed with her.

(Left) *She did not disappoint. With hands clasped and a smile on her face, she welcomed the crowd.*

Mother Teresa spoke. Softly. Vibrantly. Her message was one of love, repeating the good news brought to this world, that "He loves the world. That He loves you, and He loves me, and He loves that leper …"

She shared stories filled with compassion, and to this group she spoke in clear English. "A few weeks ago, two young people came to our house. They gave me lots of money and I asked them where do you get so much money?

They said two days ago we got married and before we married, we decided to have no wedding feast. To have no wedding clothes. To give the money to you to feed the people, your people. I was surprised and asked them about it. They answered, 'We wanted to share the joy of love by giving' …

"Hunger is not for bread alone. Hunger is for love …

"I will never forget one day walking down a street in London. I saw a man sitting looking very lonely, so I went right up to him. I reached for his hands. They were so cold. He looked up at me and said, 'After such a long time I'm feeling the warmth of a human hand.' And he had a smile on his face because there was someone who loved him …

"Small things are special to us … today people are so terribly busy that they have no time to even smile at each other … God speaks in the silence of the heart …

"The world has never needed peace so much as today. Where will the peace begin? …

There was more. I regret not having my notes at hand. She asked the question so quietly, yet so poignantly, capturing the hearts of all those who leaned toward her to hear every word. Reflecting, this question has haunted me for many years. We look at our world today, and still we ask: Where will the peace begin?

Mother lowered her head, then with a soft smile continues, "A few days before I came here a poor man came to our house, a poor man from the slums, and he said his only child was dying and the doctor had prescribed this special medicine that could be gotten only from England. I said I would do what I could. He gave me the prescription. Just at that moment a man came in with a basket of medicines. We have people that we send to families and they gather the leftover medicines from the people of Calcutta. This man came with the basket of half-used medicines and what was on the top of all the medicines—*that* medicine, the one that the doctor had prescribed.

"Had he come before, had he come after, I would not have seen him. But he came just at that moment.

"Out of the millions and millions and millions of children in the world, God was concerned for that little boy in Calcutta. God's concern for us is so great …

"I will pray for you, for your families, for the work *you* have to do. **I will pray for you that you grow in holiness. For holiness is not the luxury of the few. It is the simple duty for every one of us."**

There were twelve hundred people pushing (gently) to reach her hand. Others, who had already done so, struggled to retreat through the crowd, faces glowing with love.

Figure 3. *There were twelve hundred people pushing (gently) to reach her hand.*

I circled down the stairs to get some photo shots from in front of her. It was nearly an impossible task to accomplish: heads and hands bobbed constantly in and out of the field. Then, I was right there in front of her. A young girl beside me reached out to Mother and pressed Mother's hand against her cheek. Then, those sparkling dark eyes in their small earth-worn frame turned to me. Again.

The twelve hundred disappeared. My hand reached towards hers; the camera dropped to the length of its neck strap. Her grasp was firm and carried with it a warmth that tingled my knuckles and spread rapidly up my forearm.

Our locked eyes reached beyond the soft pushing and struggling of the moment, and continued into our very souls. I do not know what she found; I discovered a love so deep, a giving so great, a compassion so …

Again, words fail me. For 40 years now, I've sought to learn that compassion, to make it mine, but the lesson is never done. There are always new situations emerging, new circumstances, as each and every one of us is tossed into the challenges of life. For example, when dementia becomes the bedfellow of a loved one, and the trials of life must be addressed through this lens.

And so, in this state of growth, I defer to my poet laureate, Cindy Lee Scott, to give me the words:

Growth

Soul touch

Love so deep

Giving so great

Compassion so vast

Selflessness so complete

Immersed in the light of Truth

As a reflection, let's think about the close connection of the terms "passion" and "compassion". The authors like to think about compassion as feeling for another, and this book has delved pretty deeply into the meaning of passion, expressing or being affected by strong emotion. The prefix "com" represents "with"—the idea of bringing together. It adds an intensity. And, even a quick trip to the dictionary will bring in the idea of suffering, much like our earlier discussion when talking about passionate leadership in Chapter V. So, passion is an individuated expression, while compassion insinuates a reaching out to others with that passion, a strong emotion of feeling and caring. When lived in life, what a beautiful word is compassion! And Mother Teresa lived it.

Compassion as Part of a Continuum

The *Possibilities that Are YOU!* set of little Conscious Look Books focus on us fully becoming the co-creators of reality that we are. This is part of the Intelligent Social Change Journey, a developmental journey of the body, mind and heart. As we expand and grow, we move from the heaviness of cause-and-effect linear extrapolations, to the fluidity of co-evolving with our environment, to the lightness of breathing our thought and feelings into reality.[132]

As we navigate the linear, cause-and-effect characteristics of Phase 1 of this journey, *the quality of sympathy* is needed. Then, *the quality of empathy* is required to navigate the co-evolving liquidity of Phase 2. And, as we move into Phase 3, *the quality of compassion* is needed to navigate the connected breath of the creative leap.

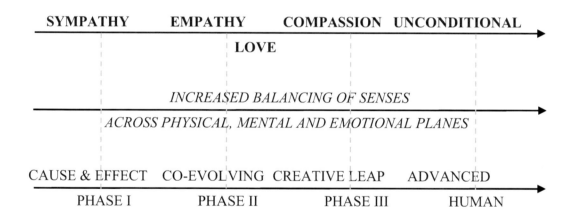

From sympathy to unconditional love:
A continuum with an increasing depth of connection.[133]

The movement from sympathy to empathy to compassion to unconditional love can be slowed or stopped through compassion fatigue, a loss or loosening of sympathy for the misfortune of others because too many demands have been made on the feelings of an individual. This is an *overwhelment* that can harden the heart. An example is the actions of some military members during World War II, and interrogators engaged in military prisons, whose belief sets did not support their actions. We have seen a great deal of overwhelment during 2020 and 2021 as the pandemic and economic downturn has affected so many lives.

This did not happen to Mother Teresa. Even when she entered what she described as "the dark night of the soul", she did not lose her faith, and her persistence in her call within a call did not falter. The extraordinary set of actions that created the pattern of her life serve as an example for us all.

Alex's emotions run deep as she recalls those special moments in her life. Emotions are a building block of consciousness. Indeed, we live "within a sea of experienced and expressed emotions."[134] We live in a sea of passion.

And as they have learned and expanded their consciousness through those experiences of passion, their energy has increasingly turned to others, As Cindy expresses:

GOLDEN CONSCIOUSNESS

Away from all of the world's confusing refashion,
Allow us to bask in love's essential compassion
So, our spirits may soar, using ethereal wings,
And we may see the beauty that life on Earth brings.

As we are moving to a higher dispensation
All life on this planet, including every nation,
United in thought away from lasciviousness
Moving life on earth to a Golden Consciousness.

What lies ahead of us is not a physical fight
People must learn to distinguish darkness from the light.
As minds and bodies move into a divergent state
Together, the darkness we can illuminate!

Look for the light in life
And in others

As they age, now in a position to look back over their histories, linking together experiences and more fully creating the story of their lives, everything seems to make more sense. And both recognize that the nearing end of these stories are the beginnings of other stories. Living in these times where life has become more uncertain for the vulnerable, those inner beliefs make life not only sustainable, but joyful for every moment of living.

Recently, Alex shared a lucid dream with Cindy about her beloved friend, partner and husband, David. In the dream, she was sitting in a lecture room, near the center about four rows back. Beside her sat David's much-loved daughter, who had transitioned several years earlier. "It's alright to cry," the daughter whispered softly to Alex.

So many people … the room was full … and they were all different ages, colors and sizes, softly whispering one to the other, somehow connected. And then, each one, one by one, turned to look up at Alex, and gradually, in a continual wave of faces, the achievements of David were shared. From this sharing, the verse "As the fire dims …" was voiced, a gift to Alex from Cindy.

As the fire dims …

As the lucid fire dims, the bright embers still glow.
An accounting is taken of this past stage show.
Untold paths illumined by this soldier's light
Gleaning, gaining, growing from a life of insight.

When each questing soul touched in turn lights up one more
Continued effect, unimaginable score.
Know that this light warrior has sharing left to do
In the dispensation that is just out of view.

VIII: Music as Passion Voiced

Music and the human mind have a unique relationship that is not yet fully understood. As Hodges forwards, "through music we are able to discover, share, express, and know about aspects of the human experience that we cannot know through other means." He goes on to say that the insights we can learn about the human condition through music are so unique and such powerful experiences that they "cannot be replaced by any other form of experience."[135] Amen.

Many researchers claim that the brain in hardwired for music! A biologist even goes so far as to say that "all of us have a biologic guarantee of musicianship, the capacity to respond to and participate in the music of our environment."[136] When Alex read that, she figured that biologist never met her mother, who couldn't carry a tune, much less even sing a note, although her mom and dad certainly could dance together, especially those unique Greek line dances!

THAT is worth noting in the context of this book. Neither of Alex's adoptive parents had any talent in that area, although certainly they were appreciators of music. Yet both the older older sister (Barbara) and Alex, growing up in a non-musical family, became musicians at some level. Barbara was a pianist, guitarist, violinist. Alex was a pianist, flautist, opera singer. Cindy, growing up in diverse family situations, but none where music was a primary focus, was a pianist, harpist, vocalist and composer. What does that say for nature versus nurture?

There are a number of proofs that support the biological basis for music. First, it is universal, throughout history and across cultures.[137] Second, music reveals itself early in life. Even infants three months old have the ability to learn and remember to move an overhead crib mobile when music is played,[138] and within a few months can recognize repeated melodies and tones.[139] Third, music exists in other animals besides humans. Monkeys can form musical abstractions.[140] And fourth, the brain has specialized areas for music.

Of specific interest to the relationship of music and passion, is that the limbic system and subcortical region of the brain—the part of the brain involved in long-term memory—are both engaged in musical and emotional responses, i.e., the link between passion and music! And this is why, of course, that when information is tied to music, it has a better chance of being encoded in long-term memory.[141] And, people have high recall when music is played during learning and that same music is played during recall.[142]

Music combines mind and body processes into one experience. For example, in a study of surgeons it was found that background music increased their alertness and concentration.[143] Conversely, it has also been found that stimulating music can serve as a distraction and interfere with cognitive performance.[144] Thus, different types of music produce different effects in different people in regard to learning.

Perhaps not surprisingly, music "may be a valuable tool for the integration of thinking across both brain hemispheres"[145] since brain function is enhanced through increased cross-callosal communication between the two hemispheres of the brain.[146]

> Music combines mind and body processes into one experience, and helps integrate thinking across the two hemispheres of the brain.

Since music has its own frequencies, it can either resonate or be in conflict with the body's rhythms. The pulse (heart beat) of the listener tends to synchronize with the beat of the music being heard (the faster the music, the faster the heartbeat). "When both are resonating on the same frequency, we fall 'in sync,' we learn better, and we're more aware and alert."[147]

Some music offers an even greater opportunity to heighten our conscious awareness in terms of sensory inputs, expand our awareness of, and access to, that which we have gathered and stored in our unconscious, and grow and expand our mental capacity and capabilities. An example is hemispheric synchronization, the use of sound coupled with a binaural beat to bring both hemispheres of the brain into unison.[148] What can occur during hemispheric synchronization is a physiologically reduced state of arousal while maintaining conscious awareness, brainwave coherence, and the capacity to reach the unconscious creative state through the window of consciousness.[149] For example, listening to a special song in your life can draw out deep feelings and memories buried in your unconscious.

Wow! That was a lot. But as you can see—and as many of you have experienced—music has the ability to connect with your deepest passions. Cindy and Alex wrote about their special relationships with music as an integral part of their lives. This first poem is a quick treatment from a young Alex.

> Shining light filters through
> The window's breathing panes.
> And far below
> The streets lay dark,
> Yet notes flow through their lanes.
>
> Hark! The chapel's belly's bursting,
> Music swells inside.
> Staffs and measures
> Make up tunes,
> And with them I will ride.

It's an interesting sidenote that very little of Alex's work is titled, while Cindy felt the necessity to name each piece. While Cindy attributes this to her OCD, in reality both sisters exhibit traits that could be related to this condition, so this may or may not be the cause. Still, it serves as an interesting comparison. "Live the Music" is an early life verse by Cindy.

Live the Music

Flat sixth, flat seventh, lifting the soul
Upward bound, a weaving roll
Shed the puppet strings
See what the music brings
Soar high, clearing the mind
Peering beyond the subconscious blind.

Flat sixth, flat seventh, up octave two
Waking the inner most you
Songs of jubilee
Lost in euphony
Bathed in sounds so glorious
Surrendered, meek and victorious.

In her beautiful poem called "Rhythms,", Cindy *listens* to the rhythms and melodies of life, those rhythms that are ever connecting us to higher patterns from which love emerges. The movie *August Rush* so beautifully expressed this concept.

RHYTHMS

Swirling, whirling sounds from everywhere
Pulling my thoughts, spinning here and there
As the wind through the chattering leaves doth blow
Gives feeling to life's breathing of ebb and flow
Turning of earth sets into motion
Rhythmic waves crashing the bleached ocean.

The warmth of the day's sunrise bringing
Intertwined morning song birds singing
A waterfall's powerful rumbling sound
Mesmerizing patterns of rain hit the ground
A gentle stream's flow, finding its way,
Setting the rhythm for a new day.

Steady cadence of the heart beating
In this compulsive life so fleeting,
Pulsating through veins as the red blood courses
Many sensations call forth new life forces.
Rhythm of converging hearts surges,
A driven pattern from which love emerges.

Moving into mid adulthood, music was a central part of both Alex's and Cindy's lives. Alex was married to a musician (composer, violinist, pianist), served as a soloist in a diversity of churches—including the Old Mission in Santa Barbara, sang in and directed musicals, and, with her musician husband, entertained at small and large events for extra income, often bringing her children into these experiences. Alex wrote the lyrics—and often the melodies—for these events. For example, when expecting her first child:

> A little girl, or little boy
> I wonder what the months will bring me?
> Your father's eyes, your mother's nose
> And hair as red as it can be.
>
> [Interlude]
> Please be good, please be strong
> Never cry from fear.
> Say your prayers, never cease
> Growing every year.
>
> A smiling face, a healthy grin
> And sparkling eyes that say you love me.
> But most of all, be everything
> Your father wishes you will be.

The songs they wrote and performed followed the events of life. For example, after one interaction, Alex wrote and sang: *You laughed at me. Yesterday you laughed at me. I was only joking, as I do. Just pretending, and you knew. But you laughed at me. Yesterday you laughed at me. And, then, today I laughed at you.* As these words are recalled, the melody and chords are singing in her head, emerging from years of silence.

Cindy—who became an accomplished pianist, vocalist, harpist and guitarist—learned to sing with large coffee cans that her "Granny" would save for her. She would put the can right in front of her face and sing into the can. This way she could hear herself very clearly and make changes in her voice or pitch as needed

… so simple, but it worked! Her "Granny" signed her up for piano lessons after buying an old out-of-tune piano. Cindy loved it and spent many hours playing that old piano. She got an old hymnal from the church and would pick out her favorite hymns note by note.

Later, as a hippie, she learned how to make her own hand-made drum, and began playing rhythms. At one place she stayed for a while, there was a large scrub tree by the steps off the front porch that had leaves growing off large stems. These made great rhythm sticks. She hollowed out the bendable green stems and, when they dried completely, the wood hardened and changed color. The two hollowed-out wooden sticks made a unique sound when gently brought together at an angle with just the right touch. So, Cindy began making these rhythm sticks, first whittling off the outer bark with a sharp knife and then burrowing out the center with a straightened-out coat hanger. It was tedious but fulfilling, and when they were done they were a lovely blond wood color, vibrating when brought together, with the sound carrying through the hollowed middle like a megaphone.

When living in San Francisco, Cindy would go to Market Street in front of the old Walgreens and sit on the sidewalk with a rope tied to her waist and to her young son. She would open her guitar case and play folk music, and people would stop to listen and even throw coins into her case. If she got enough money from the playing and singing, then the two of them would have lunch at the food bar in Walgreens.

Music continued to play a critical role in Cindy's life. In the next phase of her experience, with her partner and, until his death, good friend Mike, who had muscular dystrophy and was confined to a wheelchair, she would spend hours singing and playing music together. Cindy kept some song lists, and they played and sang from coffee house to coffee house. They both wrote their own songs. One particular song remains vivid in Cindy's memory. She can still hear Mick singing the first line: "GOING BACK DOWN TO THE OLD FARM ONE MORE TIME".

Even when life was at its hardest, Cindy found moments of joy to laugh and write and play the music of her heart. One such moment was in a refuge where she met Ismima Nepkata, who was always laughing and wore hose that had holes in them. Ismima would point at the holds and laugh and dance. So, Cindy could

not help but to write a song about her, which became a favorite as her children
grew up.

Is—ma—mi—ma, go, hi—ma, hi—ma girl
Panty Hose, Holi—ho—ho, hose—y holes
Chocolate eclairs and more in her purse.

She paints her pictures with a laugh so fair
As she shows those ho—li holes in her hose
Stop at the top, take a peek, shows it all.

Her name means inspired with sole power
To enhance the universe and you know
She likes to show those holes in her hose.

Is—mi—ma, you can just call me Meme;
With those holes, it is still your panty hose;
Ismima Nepkata, smilin' and wearin' those
hose.

Cindy continued her music, and went on to become a church musician,
playing the piano and writing original music for services, many of which were led
by her daughter. In this photo Cindy is at the keyboard.

And Alex? Not so long ago, there are so many old pieces of hand-written music
Alex discovered in a cardboard box, much of it embedded with melodies, but
other pieces that are not in her recall. While living in Santa Barbara, California,
when her children were young, Alex worked with the Camp Fire Girls, directing
a large production of *The Wizard of Oz*, running summer programs, and in 1980
running a Theatre Arts Workshop for dozens of kids of all ages. The workshop
set out to touch on all the aspects of theatre, combining the arts of music, drama,
mime, puppetry and stage movement as well as experiences working on sets,
props and costumes. Over the course of five weeks, "The Dreams of Ellen and
Charles" emerged, an original musical experience created for this unique group
of children. They expressed their desires—that is, roles they would like to play
on stage such as pirates, a princess, a spy and puppets—and things they would

like to sing about such as bubblegum, cookies and French onion soup (that was a hard one) and dreams. Thus emerged such great hits (at least for this event) as:

"I Love Bubblegum": *Bubblegum. It squishes when you chew. You only get the rotten taste when it is hard and new. But when it's reached a softer pulp and filled your mouth up some, You'll never have a better time than chewing bubblegum.*

"When Your Cookie Crumbles (Call in the Soup!)": *When the ants are getting hungry and a roach becomes your friend, And your final cookie crumbles which you find you cannot mend, Then you know your lives as pirates are coming to an end, And it's time to cut the sweets and join the French. Crumble.*

"What It Is to Be a Pirate": *Piracy is a hard, hard lot. We suffer pain and we give it all we got. If you have a scar or a tiny scab, You can join us now and help us brag.*

"A Queen's Lullaby": *A lovely moon sends the dark away. So, face your fears in the light of day. Pray tender rest to come your way. And a gentle breeze to kiss your face. The eyes of love urge us on to life, To live with faith through the darkest strife, To bring great joy to man and wife, And the sweetest child to the human race. Gentle breeze blow where you may, For my little child is resting well today.*

Two puppeteers with marionettes (with the two smallest children acting as marionettes) narrate the story, and perhaps the purpose and message of the event is best summed up in "The Controller's Lament": *Perhaps you think my job is dull, And I'm missing out on things, But what better way to glide through life Than by pulling all the strings. Too bad it takes so long to learn (And so many never do) That our puppets show the way for us, As your children do for you.* And finally, the experience ends up with a chorus of "We've All Had Fun". There is not room (or probably enough interest on the reader's part) to include it all here, although Alex would be pleased to share this material with anyone interested.

Later in life, while living in Japan and as the Music Director for the Chapel of Hope in Yokosuka, and with the help of a wonderful pianist/accompanist, Alex created special music for Christmas and Easter. It's so much fun to look at it now. One that is particularly interesting—and again way too long to include here—is called "An Ordinary Birth". It begins with a solo: *This night a brilliant star has fallen to the earth And landed in a stable through an ordinary birth. A mother and a father have been chosen from the true To raise this son of God who has come for me and you.* [Which becomes the Refrain]

The other players in this oft-told story are then introduced: *And the people crowding round the manger full of straw Are contemplating consequences of the things they saw. Angels came to shepherds and singing filled the air. Wise men chased a star but most men didn't care. He slumbers on in silence as each man thinks his thoughts, Smiling in all innocence, forgiving all their faults.* [Refrain]

Now Mary and Joseph have a duet that begins *He's our son, yet the Son. Worthy may I be. He's so small and yet he's all. He's come for you and me ...* And the shepherds have their moment of thought:

> *Lanky shanks. Even as a baby he has lanky shanks.*
> *That's good. (That's good.)*
> *Lanky shanks are better when you're roaming through the fields and woods.*
> *That's good. (That's good.)*
>
> *Solid hands. Even as a baby he has solid hands.*
> *That's good. (That's good.)*
> *Solid hands to gently find the burrs and pull them through the fur.*
> *He could! (That's good.)*
>
> *Broad shoulders. Even as a baby he has broad shoulders.*
> *He should. (That's good.)*
> *Broad shoulders will carry all the newborn lambs and keep them safe.*
> *That's good. (That's good.) ...*

This is where the wisemen get their opportunity. *Education. Education. Give this child the golden rod. Explanation. Explanation. Who will teach this Son of God?*

And finally, all four groups sing together, moving into the final refrain: *And the people crowding round this manger full of straw Are contemplating consequences of the things they saw. This night a brilliant star has fallen to the earth And landed in a stable through an ordinary birth.*

At the end, running to the manger, the children laugh, with each child who wanted a line having a line to say. *He's a baby! He's so little. Where's his crown? How can he be a prince without a crown? Where's his gold? How can he be a king without any gold? He's cold. Did he shudder? Wrap him closer. He's a baby.*

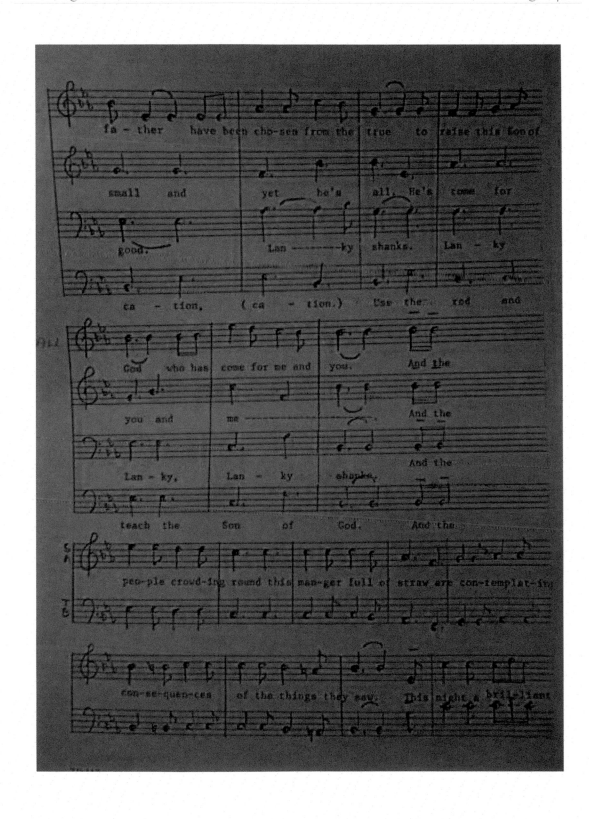

In an Easter offering called "He is Risen", I have added the name of Kenneth Hargreaves to the music (note Dean was my last name at that time), for Ken helped in so many ways with all the arrangements, and even though he was not in Japan in 1985 when I wrote this out, it is largely his music as well. Nothing is really owned by one of us. So many conversations and experiences that make us who we are today, that enable us to do the things we do, write the things we write. So, I acknowledge this musician's contribution to the music that emerged through these years, and offer it here for you.

As can be seen, music played an integral role in the early adulthood of both Cindy and Alex. And while this continued for Cindy, a life interlude occurred for Alex in this regard.

In her youth—and into her early 30's—Alex was very much an empath, living through strong undulating emotions. Upon her return from Japan to the States, struggling to become her own person, she silenced her emotions deep within and turned away from her music. That avenue of expression, that release of passion, became still.

Alex pushed herself into situations requiring a higher level of mental thought, forcing her to learn in order to survive. It was only after years of education—and when she had successfully navigated demanding work requirements—that she finally brought her two halves together and became a whole person. Here is the moment that happened.

In the early 1990's, Alex was serving as Director of Communications, Education and Training for Acquisition Reform in the U.S. Department of Navy. "Acquisition" refers to major programs encompassing millions of dollars, that is, the development and production of ships and weapons programs spread over many years. "Acquisition Reform" included more than 50 initiatives that affected the entire Acquisition process across the whole Department of Defense. It was a big job that didn't have limits, with her often working 12-14 hours or more every day of the week. And there was a fair amount of travel, although not the weekly national and international trips that occurred a few years later when Alex became the Chief Knowledge Officer of the Department.

On one occasion, there were some 20 initiatives that the Department of Defense was advancing and wanted implemented immediately. Some of these were quite challenging and going to take a lot of effort on a lot of people's part. The system was already in flux, with implementation issues emerging daily, so there were waves of frustration and irritation moving through an already overwhelmed workforce.

Alex was scheduled to speak at a Marine Corps event in Georgia, and had been invited as both the keynote and lunchtime speaker. The day was miserable in terms of weather, rain and thunder. Her flight was scheduled to leave around 7 in the evening, and she was racing through a number of deadlines to make that flight, taking a few minutes here and there throughout the day to review her speech and jot down new ideas. She was pleased when she made it to the airport on time, only to sit on the tarmac for well over an hour before the plane could take off.

She was to change planes in Atlanta, and would have just made it, only as the plane came in something went wrong, so they pulled up and went around again, finally successfully landing about five minutes after her connecting flight had departed, with the next flight early the following morning. OK. She was given a room for the night, only they couldn't find her luggage for several hours. When it finally showed up, there was only time for a shower in the room before she had to return to the airport and check back in. OK. Not bad. Gave her plenty of time to go over her speech as she waited, and she did just that, fine-tuning it and beginning to feel better about what she was going to say.

The short connecting flight went well, that is other than having to hand-search the luggage since the scanning machines were down. Oh, hum. Still, Alex arrived in plenty of time, and someone was there to pick her up and take her to the event. There were multi hundreds and hundreds of people, including vendors. By this time Alex's "speech" had been changed and corrected almost as many times as there were people (well, that may be a BIT exaggerated). Still, it was a crisscrossed mess of corrections. One vendor noted that, and quickly volunteered a "submergible" computer he was displaying. These were the days when people didn't carry their own laptops. Were there laptops then? I think not. But Alex did have a 3 1/2 inch disk, so she loaded it into the "submergible" and made all the corrections. Since there were not any printers around, a young Marine quickly volunteered to take the disk to the base and print off a fresh copy of the speech. How wonderful! That would help. So, off he went.

It was maybe 40 minutes before he returned with a sad face. "There's a virus on the disk!" So, he couldn't print it. OK. So, she used her scratched-up notes. Everything's fine. And that's when there was a great clap of thunder and all the lights in the convention center went dark. Lots of light still in the large room with a glass ceiling, and certainly in the vendor space with a high ceiling surrounded with windows, but dark in the halls and smaller meeting rooms … and, especially, in the bathroom! Yep, people lined up for 50 yards waiting to reach that goalpost! As the storm raged outside, there was an energy emerging, even a giddiness, as, one-by-one, people moved in and out of the bathroom, with those at the door holding it open to provide light for those inside.

The large glass-ceilinged meeting room, which on other occasions would be described as a gymnasium, was filled with round tables seating 12, each table-clothed in white falling from a striking centerpiece, which Alex can't quite pull up into memory. Still, the room was full, and now people were migrating in from the darker parts of the facility.

On the other side of the room, dressed in whites, a Navy chaplain raised his arms to the ceiling and loudly called out, "Let there be light!" Laugher bubbled around the room, and then silence as the lights flashed several times and finally lit fully. Then, applause, and now laughter accompanied by a stream of rising murmurs filled the room, energy rising to a palpable height. It was a thing of beauty, and Alex was swept into the moment, forgetting her speech and the difficult message she had to deliver.

She was served a light meal first. And then a Lieutenant Colonel rose to introduce her. He was a good warm-up act, taking full advantage of sharing the unique experiences leading up to her arrival at this event, and, indeed, his delivery was quite humorous! There was more laughter. Alex was laughing. Then, it was time to speak. And, somehow, flowing with the energy, it just happened. She laid her well-handled papers down on the podium and, sweeping her eyes slowly around the room, spoke.

"I was somewhat confused at the invitation to come, since it was to be both as keynote and lunchtime speaker. A keynote should deliver a message—and indeed, I have a message for you. But a lunchtime speaker should be entertaining. So, we'll do that part first."

And with that, Alex took off her glasses, stepped back from the microphone, and sang four lines from a Puccini aria, with great passion, hitting and holding a high note that rattled around the room. The crowd—many still mid-meal—lept to their feet in applause. What you do not know—and what they did not know, indeed what only a handful of people Alex worked with knew—was that she had spent many of her early years studying opera.

She raised her hands slightly to silence them. "When I was 12 years old, I had the opportunity to sing the one-line child's solo in the third act of Puccini's La Bohème [sung] *Want a trumpet and a horse*. And, as Mimi died into her muff at the end of Act IV, [sung] *Addio senza rancor*, I was wrapped in the curtain watching from the sidelines, weeping, saying to myself, 'One day, one day, that will be me.' And, indeed, some 20 years later, I sang that aria on the stage of the

Metropolitan Opera. And what was there left for me to do, but to become a senior executive with the Department of the Navy?"

There was laughter. The energy was high. Now was the time. She began, "I am here to tell you that each and every one of us is capable of incredible change," and she launched into the message she had been sent to deliver. Afterwards, they stood in line for two hours for the chance to share their thoughts with her, their problems, their fears. She listened, and took notes, not making promises, but taking in their thoughts and ideas, and thanking them for their service.

And for the next couple of years, Alex often sang out a note or two in the middle of the many speeches and workshops that punctuated her work and life. There was a wholeness about it, bringing together passions of the head and heart through music.

IX: Living from the Heart

Our passions flow naturally into creating something that truly excites us. Remember Peter Senge's words, "The passion at the heart of every great undertaking comes from the deep longing of human beings to make a difference, to have an impact. **It comes from what you contribute rather than from what you get** [emphasis added]."[150] And in order to be of service to others, we must first be of service to ourselves.

> *The passion at the heart of every great undertaking comes from the deep longing of human beings to make a difference, to have an impact.*
>
> -Peter Senge

Even as a child Alex remembers always wanting to make things right, whether that was a hurt animal, an angry conversation, or turmoil in the world. This turned out to be pretty difficult sometimes. And Cindy had those same feelings.

Life just isn't that clean—and maybe if it was, we wouldn't learn as much, or understand how truly wonderful it *can* be. Just like our emotions, life can be a pendulum of ups and downs. In a particularly low point of Alex's life, she found herself in a difficult marriage, struggling with a belief set that did not include divorce while simultaneously finding herself in untenable physical situations and continuously in mental and emotional pain, literally unable to survive in this relationship.

We forget sometimes the inner strength that is within us, our natural connection with the Universe, that energy field within which we live, whether you call it a consciousness field, a Quantum field or the God field. When we call out for help, it is there. And although it may not be what we think we want, there is an unfolding of life, complete with our passions, that does occur in right timing.

Here is a story of such a cry for help, an unconscious escape clause that Alex moved into which brought her to a moment of choice, and to a recommitment to living life.

A Letter from Santa Barbara

I would like to share the moment with you. Do not be angry.

First, today was another prophetic disappointment for, according to Hoyle (I should not use that expression since you do not play cards, what I mean is according to our local and not-so-local psychics), at 1:00 PM today California was destined to suffer a major earthquake which would cause the final, rendering crack and California's subsequent slide into the ocean.

There is a hurricane up the coast. I heard about it earlier this afternoon but thought nothing of it until I headed beach-wards for my daily swim …

As I drive into the parking lot the commotion is obvious. Half a dozen large antennae stretch upwards, supported by campers and makeshift protective enclosures and at least thirty people dressed in assorted, interesting garb sit in lawn chairs or stroll up and down the parking lot greeting each other and looking oceanwards. Two Coast Guard planes pass above and to the right, out beyond the point, a cutter moves slowly across my view.

A few determined fishermen, and at least one not-so-determined, tired child tugging on his father's sleeve, stand casting lines from the pier into the angry water. A fickle breeze sends many a line back into the pilings, but the staunch fellows merely draw in the lines and cast again, continuing their efforts.

I slip out of the thongs on my feet and feel the cool sand in between my toes as I head toward the water. The beach is empty of people. Under my feet passes the inevitable product of man (dented soda cans, wrinkled candy wrappers, crushed cigarette butts, tar) and the less-offensive litter of the ocean (broken shells, assorted pieces of wood). When I raise my head, I see the piles of kelp artistically disseminated along the shore. Seagulls (obviously of the salt water variety) stretch along the ocean in groups, parallel to the raging waters, but never venture into one another's individual space. They remind me of the stage director's inevitable lecture about body space.

The waters are rising; the tide is coming in. I can see the swirled, imprinted sand which will shortly be filled with water and, afterwards, become tidepools full of the wonders of the ocean. I toss my thongs onto the sands and slip out of the bodysuit I am wearing.

There is much hidden debris below the churning water; my feet encounter it as I run into the ocean. Small pieces of matter bang into my ankles and calves as a wave begins to break at my head. I dive into it to avoid the full impact and for a moment my oceanward trek is halted and I am held in suspension. Then the tension is released, the reversing current tugs me outward and I struggle to the surface for a breath.

I use a powerful sidearm stroke to go up and over the next breaking wave and into the choppy water beyond, then continue outward with a simpler quieter breaststroke. There is no easy spot, no opportunity for a snooze or rest upon my back, the swirling up and down waters require full strength in every stroke to avoid a dunking. Still, I am determined to reach the pier's end.

It is impossible to maintain a straight line, the waves drive me to the left and inward, the undertow to the right and outward. My body is bounced up and down and I cannot help but smile in remembrance of your loving. It is uncontrollable. Still, I plunge outward.

A detached, drenched leaf of kelp is tossed into my hair, a dead fish surfaces within an arm's reach but rapidly disappears into the fickled water. Bubbles break the surface as my arms and legs work to maintain my balance.

I glance backwards to the beach. It is empty. I know there are many people up in the lot and, in the distance, see forms still fishing from the pier. The fading blue sky has puffs of white crossing here and there but, for the most part, is calm and serene. As my head swings around I can see Santa Cruz in the distance, though a fog is rolling in and soon the island will be undiscernible.

I reach a bouncing buoy, tap it, give up attempting the pier's end, and instead head to my right toward a second buoy. I am swimming across the waves, rising and falling; I have only been in the water twenty minutes but my arms and legs ache with the effort, I am rapidly tiring and a refreshing back float is an impossibility in this roughness. I try anyway but am immediately plunged downwards. I fling my limbs and resurface, enjoying the ocean's surge of energy but wary now, and tiring.

The second buoy is in front of me, I tap it and turn towards shore. Now I ride the waves. They shoot me forward and then I lose ground as the current reverses, then again forward. The exhilaration of being totally dependent on my own volition! There is a small, nagging part of me that feels fear, that recognizes the power of the ocean, that knows there is the possibility of not returning. *Is this what I intended?* Another part shouts with freedom. I am alone, in the very midst of nature's power. I can feel the strength, the cold, I can taste the salt. A third part accepts the ocean's caresses with passion. How wonderful to slide down and into her arms! To become a part of that raging yet soft entity. *Is this what I intended?* **No!**

All these thoughts as I catch the crest of a breaking wave and am plummeted into the shore. The surging waters rip the very suit from my chest and press my own hair into my mouth. But I smile as I plant my feet upon the sands and varied debris. For in a small way I have felt, and become a part of, nature's very core, and have emerged.

With all that I am, I love you.

Around this same time in life, Cindy, struggling to find her way, created an inner realm that provided her the inner peace she sought. Here is her description of that world. And, should you choose, she invites you to join her there.

MEDITATIVE HOME

Let me take you to a peaceful place in my mind, where I go to get away from this life race. A safe and comfortable inner world called by the name, "My Place". The house sits off the ground on stilts, high enough that anyone could sit under. Water flows like a brook beneath the house which comes with heavy rains and thunder.

A home made of bamboo, and wicker, with throw rugs on the wooden floors. The walls are filled with shuttered windows and all four sides of the house have doors. My feet feel finely finished bamboo floors as I walk out onto the porch. All the screened decks surround the house, and both sides of every door have a torch.

The veranda supports aged wicker benches for sitting and resting at the end of day. There are soft cushions and blankets for warmth with throw pillows where your head can lay. A gentle breeze catches soothing sounds from many different kinds of hanging chimes. When you walk down the stairs, surrounding the home, there are trees including oranges and limes.

The bedroom contains lots of blankets on an enticing, comfy bed. Pulling the comforter up to my neck, the fluffy pillows welcome my head. I drift off to sleep listening to cricket songs floating through the cool night, dreaming of the warm distant beach waiting for me in the morning sunlight.

Waking up to morning song birds with a breeze rustling through the leaves, daybreak peers through the darkened shadows of the fading nighttime trees. Bare feet gliding down the wood stairs, reaching the soft grassy land, following the forest path till at last, the path opens to the ocean sand.

Coming out of the sheltered forest during this tranquil morning sunrise hour, the sounds of waves fill my senses with the ocean's overwhelming power. Digging my feet into the warm sand, with the sea breeze gently cooling me, I sit watching the perfect sunrise while sipping on my hot herbal tea.

Heading back, my thoughts shift and focus on likely visitors expected this day. I gather fruit and chamomile for tea in hopes that new and old friends might stay. What a wonderful place for one to come for a much-needed rejuvenation. I could forever stay in this meditative home, embracing a permanent vacation!

A peaceful dwelling.

It's been so many years since Alex made her commitment to life, and since Cindy created the inner world that provided her respite from a difficult life. Where did that time go? Indeed, as their experiences multiplied and their consciousnesses expanded, both Alex and Cindy have had full lives—living those lives with passion. And as time passed, both found special places in the natural settings of our planet. Do you feel passion for the beauty of the Earth? For Cindy it was the ocean; for Alex it was the mountains. What does your special place look like?

Cindy's Special Place

Alex's Special Place

And, as with all of our lives, special events—birthdays, holidays, vacations, graduations—were entwined with the more mundane functions of life. Here are Alex's words when her daughter graduated.

It's me standing there.
Face shining with excitement,
a slight smile curling up the ends
of a mouth waiting to be heard.

Inside is a mountain.
One side anxious to break into full bloom,
another slop still mounted on shale
awaiting the eruption of experience
to solidify.

And all topped with the beauty
– and unmarred surface –
of fresh snow.

Deep underneath are planted
the early years of love,
reassurance and encouragement.
And the comforting seeks of knowledge
still budding into application.

And perhaps mingled in –
a bit of fear?

It's me standing there.
Years ago, before the decisions were made.
And today – it's mine standing there.

Ah! And the special moments continue even as we age—sometimes gracefully and sometimes, well, not so gracefully. Alex wrote this to David on the occasion of their 15th Christmas together.

We are explorers …

Daring to charge out of our safe paradigms,
Throwing aside the good sense that was the past
And embracing unknown regions of the Universe.

We are learners …

Reading, writing, growing new ideas,
Seeing the potential and possibilities of a new world
And sharing what we learn with others.

We are lovers …

Moving beyond the other to the one,
Vibrating in ecstasy on an eternal journey of change
And recognizing the fullness of who we are.

We are.

What does living a full life mean? Yes, experiencing all the defining moments, special events, moments of joy—these are all part of our awakening, becoming aware of *who we are* and becoming the co-creators *that we are*. Perhaps this is best captured in Cindy's poem "Consciousness Rising."

CONSCIOUSNESS RISING

Awakening to the world
Awareness of who you are
Conscious of life around you

Learning how to love others
Sharing our lives together
Balancing the emotions

Knowing the earth also lives
Seeing what needs to be done
Making a greater difference

Looking inward to the soul
Clearing away all the weeds
Maturing in the spirit

Giving back to those in need
Preparing for the journey
Returning to the presence

Embracing Life!
Embracing Love!
Living!

And there are lots of dreams along the journey of life—waking and sleeping. When Alex's partner David and she had completed building the Mountain Quest complex—a vision, a passion of David's of which she had happily become a part—Alex had a series of celebratory dreams that she thoroughly enjoyed. In these dreams, she was stepping off of the top rung of a ladder into a room bubbling with happiness. In front of her was a table full of presents, and she knew these were for her. But for several nights her dream would end just as she was beginning to open the presents, so she would patiently wait until the following night, hoping to see what was in them.

On the third night, just as she was finally making some headway with opening a present, the table slid away and there was another ladder in front of her, calling her to step upon the first rung. So, she did, and everything around her changed—she was on a new journey. The message was clear. *What we think is the end is always a new beginning in a beautiful cycle of living and learning.*

We live in a world today that has destructive tendencies. We've all been drawn into these dark times. Yet, there is light in the distance … It was from this frame of reference that Cindy penned "Holocene Extinction".

Holocene Extinction

We are in the midst of a Holocene Extinction.
Poor, wealthy, strong or great, the earth makes no distinction.
Thousands of plants and animals dying off each year;
Man continues living, assuming nothing to fear.

An unprecedented global super predator,
Mother Earth has become Humanity's creditor.
Human beings' impact on the environmental
Is leaving a life deficit that's monumental.

Anthropogenic influences without any stops,
Transmission of diseases through livestock and crops.
Population growth, Industrial Revolution,
What's needed *now* is an altruistic solution.

With human growth, and oceanic devastation,
Habitat destruction and vast deforestation;
All leading to an understanding of exactly how;
We've reached the Holocene event that we're facing now.

An eminent mass extinction, the sixth, maybe more,
The end of life, as we know it, knocking at the door.
But, wait! We continue on, and everything is fine;
For, the corporeal can transform to crystalline.

Then, in the midst of these challenges, there was the surprise and unbridled joy of meeting a sister who—at least one of us—didn't know existed! This moment of passion occurred when Cindy's children brought her to Mountain Quest, located in the hills of the Allegheny Mountains of West Virginia. Here is Cindy's verse capturing this budding relationship as we finish our lives.[151]

When I feel your strong spirit
Reaching out to mine
Our life force for just a while
Becomes intertwined.

Seeking a familiar place
Where you talk with me
We share segments of our lives
That others can't see.

You open an inner door
And invite me in
We embrace in the spirit
Sharing where we've been.

In that inner room we meet
Knowing each other
Sharing special gifts honed
With one another.

As I shared my life with you
You encounter me
Together, we know things are
just as they should be.

And in closing from Cindy: "Now that I'm coming to the end of my lifespan, at least it feels that way, the body is mostly controlled by the Parkinson's Disease. With a stiffened and aching body, I cannot override the pain as easily as I used to, but there are still times when I can rise above my affliction … I soar in the clouds during those all-too-short-but-astounding moments in time. And I am thankful for whatever is left and will continue seeking and growing until my time here is done. There is so much wonderment left for me still to discover, or maybe even new or fresh beginnings! It's been a miraculous and phenomenal journey!!!!!" And one of those learnings has been, "Everything in Balance":

Violence and love: Life's a balance of both.
Destruction fertilizes new growth
Love's nurturing spirit breeds beauty
Producing
Timeless Growth
Seeking balance

All things working together to survive,
The very act of being alive,
Too much or too little doesn't work
Equaling One Stillness
Finding balance

Everything must balance now and again
Forces of water, earth, fire and wind
Thrive together in equilibrium
Co-sharing
The Life Force
Living balance

We as humans have been given so many hints of what is yet to come. And the more we understand about the amazing human mind, the more potential we can see! For example, the reality that our thoughts can actually restructure the brain. And the phenomenon of mirror neurons, a form of cognitive mimicry that transfers actions, behaviors and most likely other cultural norms. In short, when we *see* something being enacted, whether in our external or internal environment, our mind creates the same patterns as if we were actually *doing* that "something" ourselves.[152] When you think of this through the eyes of passion, we can potentially repeat special moments over and over again!

One more story from Alex:

A few weeks ago, I was working in a support role with a large internationally renowned orchestra. My job was to make sure everyone had the sheet music they needed, run errands for the Maestro, and generally handle the small emergencies that regularly occur when you bring together nearly 60 professional musicians! How I enjoyed my work! During rehearsals I had a folding chair right behind the Maestro. And, over the years, many of these musicians had become personal friends. Just imagine being right in the middle of things as the orchestra recorded Mahler's and Tchaikovsky's symphonies. But it was the operas that tugged at my heart. I've heard it said that the first time someone attends the opera they either love it or hate it. For me, it was definitely the former.

The Maestro was well-respected, a recipient of the National Medal of Arts from the President, and the Gold Baton from the American Symphony Orchestra League. Little wonder that the owner of the theatre was sitting in the front row stage right grinning, thoroughly enjoying the rehearsal. The focus on this particular occasion was Bizet's Carmen; the last hour had been spent reviewing a few hot spots throughout the score. Now, the Maestro wiped his brow, stuck the red handkerchief in his pocket, and announced "No. 1. The Prelude." There was a slight scuffing of chairs, rattling of paper and a soft swish as bows were renewed.

By way of context, all the detail provided above is more of a knowing that all this was happening. And now, the essence of the experience.

The Maestro turned his head to give me a wink, smiled at the theatre owner, then, turning back to me, handed me the baton and said, "Take them through this. I'll be right back." And he was gone, heading out the back of stage right.

From the edge of my eye, I see the owner's mouth hanging open. But I hop right up on the rostrum and raise my arm. I glance quickly at the music. *Allegro giocoso fortissimo*. The slight smile I know is on my face expands. What fun! 2/4 time. I set the tempo with two beats and we are off and playing. Perfect staccatos. Four measures in, a perfect trill. Repeat. Now, piano. Flow, staccato, flow, staccato ... *Pianissimo, crescendo molto*. My body bounces, softly, with the rhythm, tears move down my face, coming from I know not where since I'm immersed in pure joy. I KNOW this music. I FEEL this music. And near the end we move into ¾ time *Andante moderator*, expressive movement weaving note-into-note-into-note, building to a final chord that is staccato fortississimo!

My body is shaking while simultaneously rooted in place. *Pausa lunga*. The Maestro is behind me, smiling. And then I woke up in my bed here at Mountain Quest, eyes wide open, still filled with all the joy and fullness and majesty of the experience.

How could this be? How could an experience so real happen? I began to flick back through my life experiences. Yes, I knew and had the opportunity to work with Maurice Abravanel when he joined the Music Academy of the West for summer programs. Yes, I've sung in the chorus in Carmen productions and studied the role of Micaela, so there is no doubt that at some point I've watched and heard an orchestra play the Prelude to Carmen. Yes, I've conducted choral groups, small bands and small string groups, and even the 7th Fleet Band in Yokosuka once, so the *feel* of conducting is familiar. STILL, I've never conducted a large orchestra, and certainly never the Prelude to Carmen! Yet, I JUST DID THAT, perfectly, accompanied by all the activity and feelings of the moment. Have you had this kind of experience happen to you?

Ah! So not only can we "repeat" moments of passion, but in the inner realms of our mind and perhaps our soul—an existential state—we can "create" moments of passion, building and expanding from the experiential moments of our lives! Wow!

That certainly gives us incentive to fully—and passionately—enjoy our lives! *There's a passion bank account that only accrues interest*. Even when you make a withdrawal—perhaps interconnecting moments of passion in your dream state—you are only adding MORE, that is, the passion of your dream. With knowledge, the more you share, the more you have. With passion, the more you use, the more you have to create.

As we move through the winter of our lives,

With light waning in the soft distant sky,

Embracing—even welcoming—the cold,

We've figured out the wherefor and the why.

After spending life searching everywhere

For answers to our deepest life concerns

We've discovered that you can find within

All the answers for that which your heart yearns.

Thank you for joining us on this journey. May you live and love with passion!

Endnotes

[1] The term "incluessence" was coined by Jo Dunning (August 12, 2015, email to Alex). Jo talks about "True Incluessence" as the state of our Being that is far beyond the small drop of possibility was have come to accept as true. In our usage we infer a future state that is far beyond that which we know to dream. And from Cindy:

INCLUESSENCE

A state of being far beyond
That which one can dream
Unlike anything to this day,
That's ever been seen
Believed to be the very highest
Grand level of change
Covering an unimaginable
And uncharted range!

Living, learning outside the box
Allows us to see
The way corporeal's become
All that they can be.
Tapping into the soul self with
An intuitional wing,
Getting glimpses of the essence
That is everything!

[2] Frijda, N. H. (2000). "The Psychologists' Point of View" in Lewis, M. and Haviland-Jones, J.M., *Handbook of Emotions* (2nd ed). New York: The Guilford Press, 59-74.

[3] Polanyi, M. (1958). *Personal Knowledge: Towards a Post-Critical Philosophy.* Chicago: The University of Chicago Press.

[4] Damasio, A. R. (1999). *The Feeling of What Happens: Body and Emotion in the Making of Consciousness.* New York: Harcourt Brace & Company.

[5] Goleman, D. (1995). *Emotional Intelligence.* New York : Bantam Books. There are many excellent related books building on this initial offering.

[6] Plotkin, H. (1994). *Darwin Machines and the Nature of Knowledge.* Cambridge, MA: Harvard University Press, p. 211.

[7] Bennett-Goleman, T. (2001). *Emotional Alchemy: How the Mind can Heal the Heart.* New York: Harmony Books.

[8] Belitz, C. and Lundstrom, M. (1997). *The Power of Flow.* New York: Harmony Books.

[9] Melendez, S.E. (1996). "An Outsider's View of Leadership" in Hesselbein, F., Goldsmith, M. & Beckhard, R. *The Drucker Foundation: The Leader of the Future.* San Francisco: Jossey-Bass, pp. 293-302.

[10] Senge, Peter (1990). *The Fifth Discipline*. New York: Doubleday.

[11] Marinoff, L. (2003). *The Big Questions: How Philosophy Can Change Your Life*. New York: Bloomsbury.

[12] Adler, M. J. (1992). *The Great Ideas: A Lexicon of Western Thought*. New York: Scribner Classics.

[13] Frijda, p. 6.

[14] Ibid.

[15] Honderich, T. (1999). The Philosophers: Introducing Great Western Thinkers. Oxford: Oxford University Press, p. 110.

[16] Adler, p. 185.

[17] Barnhardt, R.K. & Steinmetz, S. (1988). *Chambers Dictionary of Etymology*. New York: Chambers, p. 761.

[18] Oxford English Dictionary (5th Ed) (2002). Volumes 1 and 2. Oxford: Oxford University Press.

[19] Frijda, p. 59.

[20] Belitz and Lundstrom, p. 57.

[21] Ibid.

[22] Goleman, D. (1995), p. 228.

[23] Csikszentmihalyi, M. (2003). *Good Business: Leadership, Flow and the Making of Meaning*. New York: Viking, p. 60.

[24] Gyatso, T. (The Fourteenth Dalai Lama) (1992). *The Meaningful of Life: Buddhist Perspectives on Cause and Effect*. Boston: Wisdom Publications. Also, Walsh, R. and Shapiro, D.H. (1983). *Beyond Health and Normality: Explorations of Exceptional Psychological Well-Being*. New York: Van Nostrand Reinhold Company. Also, Watts, A.W. (2002). *ZEN: The Supreme Experience: The Newly discovered Scripts*. London: Vega.

[25] Rockwell, I. (2002). *The Five Wisdom Energies: A Buddhist Way of Understanding Personalities, Emotions, and Relationships*. Boston: Shambhala, p. 52.

[26] Belitz and Lundstrom.

[27] Csikszentmihalyi, M. (1990). *Flow: The Psychology of Optimal Experience*. New York: Harper Perennial, p. 4.

[28] Csikszentmihalyi, M. (1990), p. 3.

[29] Csikszentmihalyi, M. (2003), p. 39.

[30] Csikszentmihalyi, M. (2003), p. 60.

[31] Belitz and Lundstrom, p. 57.

[32] Ibid.

[33] Ibid.

[34] Goleman (1995), p. 228.

[35] The KMTL Study is a 2005 research study that reached out to 34 Knowledge Management Thought Leaders located across four continents. The intent was to explore the aspects of KM that contributed to the passion expressed by these thought leaders.

[36] Bennet, A., Bennet, D. and J. Lewis (2018). Leading with the Future in Mind: Knowledge and Emergent Leadership. Frost, WV: MQIPress, p. 236.

[37] This material was first made available in Bennet, A., Bennet, D., Shelley, A., Bullard, T. and J. Lewis (2020). *The Profundity and Bifurcation of Change Part III: Learning in the Present*. Frost, WV: MQIPress. (Used with permission)

[38] Meriam-Webster (2016).

[39] MacFlouer, N. (1999). *Life's Hidden Meaning*. Tempe, AZ: Ageless Wisdom Publishers.

[40] Carey, K. (1996). *The Third Millennium: Living in the Posthistoric World*. New York: HarperCollins Publishers, p. 30.

[41] Frankl, V.E. (1939/1963). *Man's Search for Meaning: An Introduction of Logotherapy*. New York: Pocket Books, pp. 58-59.

[42] Frankl, p. 160.

[43] *The Urantia Book* (1955). Chicago: URANTIA Foundation, p. 1098.

[44] Sternberg, R.J. (1986). "A Triangular Theory of Love" in *Psychological Review 93* (2): 119-135.

[45] Barsade, S. and O'Neill, O.A. (2014). "What's Love Got to Do with It? A Longitudinal Study of the Culture of Companionate Love and Employee and Client

Outcomes in a Long-term Care Setting" in *Administrative Science Quarterly* 59(4) (November), 551-598, p. 2.

[46] There is a direct correlation between the continuum moving from sympathy to empathy to compassion to unconditional love and the phase changes of the Intelligent Social Change Journey (ISCJ), which is a developmental journey of the body, mind and heart. As we expand and grow, we move from the heaviness of cause-and-effect linear extrapolations, to the fluidity of co-evolving with our environment, to the lightness of breathing our thought and feelings into reality. Along with the movement from linear cause and effect to co-evolving with our environment, it is necessary to deepen our understanding of others, thus moving from sympathy to empathy. And as we move through co-evolving and towards recognition of the larger ecosystem of which we are a part, an ever-deepening connection emerges as compassion. It is through compassion that we begin to touch agápē love. See Bennet, A., Bennet, D., Shelley, A., Bullard, T. and J. Lewis (2020). *The Profundity and Bifurcation of Change* (Parts I-V). Frost, WV: MQIPress.

[47] Scott, Cindy Lee. (2021). Painting the Reality of My Soul: A Life Journey of Verse. Frost, WV: MQIPress.

[48] Seligman, M.E.P. (2011). *Flourish: A Visionary New Understanding of Happiness and Well-being*. New York: Free Press, p. 144-45.

[49] Darwin, C. (1998). *The Descent of Man*. Amherst, NY: Prometheus Books, p. 110.

[50] Kropotkin, P. (1902). *Mutual Aid: A Factor of Evolution*. London: Heinemann.

[51] Swomley, J. (2000). "Violence: competition or Cooperation." In *Christian Ethics Today 26*, Vol. 6, No. 1.

[52] Andersen, N.A. and Born, A.W. (2008). "The Employee in the Sign of Love" in *Culture and Organization* 14(4): 325-343.

[53] Cozolino, L.J. (2006). *The Neuroscience of Human Relationships: Attachment and the Developing Social Brain*. New York: W.W. Norton, p. 203

[54] Kohut, H. (1984). *How Does analysis Cure?* Eds. A. Goldberg & P. Stepansky. Chicago: University of Chicago Press.

[55] Riggio, R.E. (2015). "Are You Empathic? 3 Types of Empathy and What They Mean." Retrieved 09/14/15 from http://www.psychologytoday.com/blog/cutting-edge-leadership/201_108/are-you-empathic-3-types-empathy-and-what-they-mean

[56] Masserman, J., Wechkin, M.D., Terris, W. (1964). "Altruistic Behavior in Rhesus Monkeys." In *Am. J. Psychiatry 121*, pp. 584-85.

[57] de Waal, F. (2009). *The Age of Empathy: Nature's Lessons for a Kinder Society.* New York: Harmony Books.

[58] Augustine, J.R. (1996). "Circuitry and Functional Aspects of the Insular Lobe in Primates, including Humans." In *Brain Research Reviews, 22*, pp. 229-244.

[59] Cozolino, p. 206

[60] Andersson, J.L., Lilja, A., Hartvig, P., Langstrom, B., Gordh, T., and Handwerker, H. (1997). "Somatotopic Organization along the Central Sulcus, for Pain Localization in Humans, as Revealed by Positron Emission Tomography." In *Experimental Brain Research, 117*, pp. 192-199. Also, Calder, A.J., Beaver, J.D., Eger, E., Jenkins, R., Winston, J., Dolan, R.J. and Henson, R.N.A. (2006). "The Neural Correlates of Eye Gaze Adaptation." In *PERCEPTION 35*, pp. 240-324.

[61] eCunha, M.P., Clegg, S.R., Costa, C., Leite, A.P., Rego, A., Simpson, A.V., DeSousa, M.O. and Sousa, M. (2016). "Gemeinschaft in the Midst of Gesellschaft? Love as an Organizational Value" in *Journal of Management, Spirituality & Religion* (July), 1-19.

[62] Barsade, S. and Gibson, D. (2007). "Why Does Affect Matter in Organizations?" in *Academy of Management Perspectives 21* (1), 36-59. Also, Chartrand, T.L. and Lakin, J.L. (2013). "The Antecedents and Consequences of Human Behavioral Mimicry" in *Annual Review of Psychology* 64, 285-308. Also, Menges, J.I. and Kilduff, M. (2015). "Group Emotions: Cutting the Gordian Knots Concerning Terms, Levels of Analysis, and Processes" in *Academy of Management Annals* 9 (1), 849-932.

[63] eCunha et al., p. 8.

[64] Argandoňa, (2011). "Beyond Contracts: Love in Firms" in *Journal of Business Ethics* 99 (1): 77-85.

[65] Damasio, p. 60.

[66] Polanyi, p. 133.

[67] Ibid.

[68] Polanyi, p. 135.

[69] Descartes, René (1649). *The Treatise on the Passions of the Soul.*

[70] LeDoux, J. (1996). *The Emotional Brain: The Mysterious Underpinnings of Emotional Life.* New York: touchstone.

[71] Long, T.A. (1986). "Narrative Unity and Clinical Judgment" in *Theoretical Medicine 7*, pp. 75-92.

[72] Denning, S. (2001). *The Springboard: How Storytelling Ignites Action in Knowledge-Era Organizations.* Boston: Butterworth Heinemann, p. 113.

[73] Schank, R.E. (1990). *Tell Me a Story: Narrative and Intelligence.* Evanston, IL: Northwestern University Press.

[74] Bennet, A., Bennet, D., Shelley, A., Bullard, T. and Lewis, J. (2020). *The Profundity and Bifurcation of Change Part III: Learning in the Present.* Frost, WV: MQIPress.

[75] Pinker, S. (1997). *How the Mind Works.* New York: W.W. Norton and Company, p. 412.

[76] Pinker, pp. 412-413.

[77] Rosenthal, N.E., M.D. (2002). *The Emotional Revolution: How the New Science of Feelings Can Transform Your Life.* New York: Citadel Press Books, p. 29.

[78] Rosenthal, p. 31.

[79] Damasio.

[80] Marinoff, p. 62.

[81] Bennet, A. (2020). *Possibilities that are YOU!* (Volume 15) Wisdom. Frost, WV: MQIPress. (Model used with permission.)

[82] *The Urantia Book* (1955). Chicago: URANTIA Foundation, p. 908.

[83] Goleman, D., Kaufman, P. and Ray, M. (1992). *The Creative Spirit: Companion to the PBS Television Series.* New York: Penguin Books, p. 30.

[84] Goleman, p. 31.

[85] Csikszentmihaly, M. (1996). *Creativity: Flow and the Psychology of Discovery and Invention.* New York: HarperCollins Publishers, Inc., p. 72.

[86] Ibid.

[87] Csikszentmihaly, p. 316.

[88] Bennet, D., Bennet, A. and Turner, R. (2018). *Expanding the Self: The Intelligent Complex Adaptive Learning System.* Frost, WV: MQIPress.

[89] Leonard, D. and Swap, W. l(1999). *When Sparks Fly: Igniting Creativity in Groups*. Boston, MA: Harvard Business School Press, p. 178.

[90] Leonard and Swap, p. 182-183.

[91] Ibid.

[92] Leonard and Swap, p. 191.

[93] Amabile, T.M. (1997). "Motivating Creativity in Organizations: On Doing What you Love and Loving What You Do." In *California Management Review*, 40(1), 39-58. Also, Palanyi (1966). *The Tacit Dimension*. New York: Anchor Doubleday.

[94] Kouzes, J.M. and Posner, B.Z. (1993). *Credibility: How Leaders Gain and Lost It, Why People Demand It*. San Francisco: Jossey-Bass, p. 235.

[95] Kouzes and Posner, p. 232.

[96] Maxwell, J.C. (1999). The 21 *Indispensable Qualities of Leaders: Becoming the Person Others Will Want to Follow*. Nashville: Thomas Nelson Publishers, p. 83.

[97] Peters, T. and Austin, N. (1985) *A Passion for Excellence: The Leadership Difference*. New York: Random House, p. xix.

[98] Peters and Austin, p. xx.

[99] Batten, J. (1998). "Servant-leadership: A passion to serve." In L.C. Spears (Ed.). *Insights on Leadership: Service, Stewardship, Spirit and Servant-Leadership*. New York: John Wiley & Sons.

[100] Lad, L.J. and Luechauer, D. (1998). "On the path to servant-leadership." In L.C. Spears (Ed.). *Insights on Leadership: Service, Stewardship, Spirit, and Servant-Leadership*. New York: John Wiley & Sons, p. 60.

[101] Handy, C. (1999). "The search for meaning." In F. Hesselbein and P.M. Cohen, *Leader to Leader: Enduring Insights on Leadership from the Drucker Foundation's Award-Winning Journal*, pp. 121-132. New York: Drucker Foundation Leaderbooks, p. 131.

[102] Neff, T.J. and Citrin, J.M. (1999). *Lessons from the Top: The Search for America's Best Business Leaders*. New York: Currency Doubleday, p. 380.

[103] Ibid.

[104] Bell, C.R. (1997). "Passionate leadership." In K. Shelton (Ed.). *A New Paradigm of Leadership: Visions of Excellence for 21st Century Organizations*. Provo, UT: Executive Excellence Publishing, p. 196.

[105] Bell, p. 197.

[106] Kouzes, p. 324.

[107] Bell, p. 198.

[108] Melendez, p. 299.

[109] Senge, p. 62.

[110] Bennet, A. (2005). *Exploring Aspects of KM that Contribute to the Passion Expressed by Its Thought Leaders*. Self-published.

[111] Csikszentmihalyi, M. (1996). *Creativity: Flow and the Psychology of Discovery and Invention*. New York: HarperCollins Publishers, Inc., p. 316.

[112] Csikszentmihaly (2003).

[113] Birkinshaw, J. and Gibson (2004). "Building Ambidexterity into an Organization." In MIT *Sloan Management Review* 45(4), Summer 2004, pp. 46-55.

[114] Bennet, A. and Bennet, D. (2004). Organizational Survival in the New World: The Intelligent Complex Adaptive System. Burlington, MA: Elsevier.

[115] Battram, A. (1996). *Navigating Complexity: The Essential Guide to Complexity Theory in Business and Management*. London: The Industrial Society.

[116] Cohen, J. and Steward, I. (1994). *The Collapse of Chaos: Discovering Simplicity in a Complex World*. New York: Viking.

[117] Gigerenzer, G. and Todd, P.M. (1999). *Simple Heuristics that Make Us Smart*. New York: Oxford University Press.

[118] Battram, p. 13.

[119] Stewart, T.A. (2001). *The Wealth of Knowledge: Intellectual Capital and the Twenty-First Century Organization*. New York: Currency.

[120] Gupta, A.K. and Westney, D.E. (2003). *Smart Globalization: Designing Global Strategies, Creating Global Networks*. Boston: MIT Press.

[121] Wilson, E.O. (1998). *Consilience: The Unity of Knowledge*. London: Abacus.

[122] Bonabeau, E. and Meyer, C. (2001). "Swarm Intelligence: A Whole New Way to Think about Business." In *Harvard Business Review*, May, pp. 107-114.

[123] Walsh, R. and Shapiro, D.H. (1983). *Beyond Health and normality: Explorations of Exceptional Psychological Well-Being*. New York: Van Nostrand Reinhold Company.

[124] Watts, A. (2002). *ZEN: The Supreme Experience: The Newly Discovered Scripts*. London: Vega, p. 57.

[125] Gyatso, T., the Fourteenth Dalai Lama (1992). *The Meaning of Life: Buddhist Perspectives on Cause and Effect*. Boston: Wisdom Publications.

[126] Bennett-Goleman, T. (2001). *Emotional Alchemy: How the Mind Can Heal the Heart*. New York: Harmony Books, p. 312.

[127] Ibid.

[128] Rockwell, p. 52.

[129] Rockwell, p. 184.

[130] Marinoff, p. 58.

[131] Marinoff.

[132] For an academic treatment of the Intelligent Social Change Journey, see the five-book set: Bennet, A., Bennet, D. Shelley, A., Bullard, T. and Lewis, J. (2020). The Profundity and Bifurcation of Change. Frost, WV: MQIPress. Part I Laying the Groundwork; Part II Learning from the Past; Part III Learning in the Present; Part IV Co-Creating the Future; Part V Living the Future.

[133] Bennet, A. (2018). *Possibilities that are YOU! (Volume 4) Conscious Compassion*. Frost, WV: MQIPress. (Used with permission.)

[134] Plotkin, p. 211.

[135] Hodges, D. (2000). "Implications of Music and Brain Research" in Music Educators Journal, 87(2), 17-22, p. 21.

[136] Wilson as cited in Hodges, p. 18.

[137] Swain, J. (1997). Musical Languages. New York: W.W. Norton.

[138] Fagan, J., Prigot, J., Carroll, M., Pioli, L., Stein, A. and Franco, A. l(1997). "Auditory Context and Memory Retrieval in Young Infants" in *Child Development, 68*, 1057-1066.

[139] Weinberger, N.M. (2004). "Music and the brain." In *Scientific American, 291*, pp. 89-95. Also, Hannon, E.E. and Johnson, S.P. (2005). "Infants use meter to categorize rhythms and melodies: Implications for Musical Structure Learning." In *Cognitive Psychology, 50*, pp. 354-377.

[140] Sousa, D.A. (2006). *How the Brain Learns*. Thousand Oaks, CA: Corwin Press.

[141] Jensen, E. (2000). *Brain Based Learning: The New Science of Teaching and Training*. San Diego, CA: The Brain Store.

[142] Godden, D.R. and Baddeley, A.D. (1975). "Context-dependent memory in two natural environments on land and underwater." In *British Journal of Psychology 66*, pp. l325-331.

[143] Restack, R.M. (2003). *The New Brain: How the Modern Age is Rewiring Your Mind*. New York: Rodale.

[144] Hallom, S. (2002). "The effects of background music on studying." In Deasy, R.J. (Ed.), *Critical Links: Learning in the Arts and Student Academic and Social Development*. Arts Education Partnership, Washington, D.C., pp. 74-75.

[145] Jensen, p. 246.

[146] Thompson, R.F. (2000). *The Brain: A Neuroscience Primer*. New York: Worth.

[147] Jensen, p. 246.

[148] Bennet, A. and Bennet, D. (2008). "The human knowledge system: Music and brain coherence." In *VINE: The Journal of Information and Knowledge Management Systems, 38* (3), pp. 277-295.

[149] Atwater, F.H. (2004). *The Hemi-Sync Process*. Faber, VA: The Monroe Institute. Fischer, R. (1971). "A cartography of ecstatic and meditative state." In *Science, 174* (12), pp. 897-904. Delmonte, M.M. (1984). "Electrocortical activity and related phenomena associated with meditation practice: A literature review." In *International Journal of Neuroscience, 24*, pp. 217-231. Goleman, G.M. (1988). *Meditative Mind: The Varieties of Meditative Experience*. New York: G.P. Putnam. Jevning, R., Wallace, R.K. and Beidenbach, M. (1992). "The physiology of meditation: A review." In *Neuroscience and Behavioral Reviews*, 16, pp. 415-424. Mavromatis, A. (1991). *Hypnagogia*. New York: Routledge. West, M.A. (1980). "Meditation and the EEG." In *Psychological Medicine*, 10, pp. 69-375.

[150] Senge, p. 62.

[151] The rolling mountains of the Allegheny's provide the backdrop for the Mountain Quest Institute, where the sisters met for the first—and only—time.

[152] Bennet, A. (2018). *Possibilities that are YOU! Volume 22: Beyond Action*. Frost, WV: MQIPress.

Index

First Line Index (Stories, music, prose and poetry)

<u>MQIPress Conscious Look Books:</u>

The Possibilities that are YOU!

by Alex Bennet

All Things in Balance
The Art of Thought Adjusting
Associative Patterning and Attracting
Beyond Action
Connections as Patterns
Conscious Compassion
The Creative Leap
The Emerging Self
The Emoting Guidance System
Engaging Forces
The ERC's of Intuition
Grounding
The Humanness of Humility
Intention and Attention
Knowing
The Living Virtues of Today
Me as Co-Creator
Seeking Wisdom
Staying on the Path
Transcendent Beauty
Truth in Context

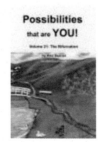

See www.possibilitiesthatareyou.net

Also,

The Intelligent Social Change Journey
by Alex Bennet, David Bennet, Arthur Shelley, Theresa Bullard and John Lewis
(Available in soft back on amazon.com)

Other books by Poet Cindy Lee Scott

How does one become a poet?

As Cindy Lee Scott begins, "Looking back, what an incredible life I've had! It is most definitely overwhelming when looking back at all the magnificent, as well as difficult, times I've been through. Yet, here I am still embracing life, fighting my battles, and growing in this never and ever-ending story of me. Dramas and comedies, sadness and elations, melancholy and exuberance, failures and victories, all forming the person I've become."

This **anthology of the work of Mountain Quest Poet Laureate Cindy Lee Scott**, includes personal stories written by the poet herself as well as objective thoughts added by Professor Dr. Alex Bennet, the Director of the Mountain Quest Institute, a research and retreat center situated in the Allegheny Mountains of West Virginia. As you will discover, although these two authors met just a few years ago and have only spent one week together, there is a special connection between the two, which provides a real-life study of nature versus nurture.

Excerpt from the Introduction by the poet:

While watching the 2016 Presidential campaign, I was shaken with extreme agitation. This reality show didn't even seem real! ... This incision-division continues to create a widening gulf between the people of our country. Even friends and families are polarized in the "who's right and who's wrong" political frenzy! ... *What's going on? How did we get here? Have I been asleep?*

This **collection of prose and poetry motifs represent my journey searching for truth** and, ultimately, discovering the beauty that can be found in change, not only politically but inwardly. I ask myself: What is freedom's definition in these changing times? And what can I do to help ensure the freedoms we so cherish? This great country with all its grand diversity is assuredly being tested. It has long been said that a house divided cannot stand. ... This is a great time of accelerated growth for humans, and, somehow, we must come together to raise our consciousness as a whole.

Made in the USA
Middletown, DE
20 June 2021